A Merry, Merry Christmas Book

Alle Littel Childer Syng

Alle littel childer syng
Prayers to our younge Kyng
Some syng sharpe and some syng flat
Alma mater Exeat.

Alle engels in ye skie
Maken loude melodie
With sackbut, organ, pipe and drum
Ad Terrorem Omnium.

Ye povre beastes in ye stalle,
Alack, they cannot syng at alle
Ne cock ne henne of either sexe
De Minimis Non Curat Lex.

OSBERT LANCASTER

A Merry, Merry CHRISTMAS BOOK

edited by Eric Posselt

decorations by Dave Lyons

Prentice-Hall, Inc.   Englewood Cliffs, N. J.

Acknowledgments

To Frank Sullivan and *The New Yorker* for permission to include "Crisp New Bills for Mr. Teagle," by Frank Sullivan, originally published in *The New Yorker*, copyright, 1935, by The New Yorker, Inc.

To Robert M. Yoder and *The Saturday Evening Post* for permission to include "Merry Christmas in Ten Pieces," copyright, 1947, *The Saturday Evening Post*.

To Harper & Brothers, New York, for "A Christmas Spectacle" from *Love Conquers All*, by Robert C. Benchley, copyright, 1922, by Harper & Brothers; renewed 1950, by Gertrude Benchley.

To E. P. Dutton & Co., Inc., New York, for "P.C.X.36" from *A Christmas Garland*, by Max Beerbohm. For "A Hint for Next Christmas" from *If I May*, by A. A. Milne, copyright, 1921, by E. P. Dutton & Co., Inc., New York; renewed 1949, by A. A. Milne. And for "Ring Out, Wild Bells," by D. B. Wyndham Lewis, from *The Christmas Companion*, copyright, 1941, by E. P. Dutton & Co., Inc.

To J. B. Lippincott Co., Philadelphia, for "Dancing Dan's Christmas" from *Blue Plate Special*, by Damon Runyon, copyright, 1932, by Damon Runyon.

To Harcourt, Brace and Co., Inc., New York, for "Mr. Kaplan and the Magi" from *The Education of Hyman Kaplan*, by Leonard Q. Ross, originally published in *The New Yorker*, copyright, 1937, by Harcourt, Brace and Co., Inc.

Acknowledgments

To Christopher Morley for "The Worst Christmas Story," originally published in *Bookman Magazine*, copyright, 1921, by George H. Doran Company; renewed 1949 by Christopher Morley.

To Dodd, Mead & Co., Inc., New York, for "The Errors of Santa Claus" from *Wet Wit and Dry Humor*, by Stephen Leacock, copyright, 1931, by Dodd, Mead & Co., Inc.

To Mary Rose Bradford for "How Come Christmas" by Roark Bradford, published by Harper & Brothers, copyright, 1930, by Roark Bradford.

To *The Atlantic Monthly* for "Alle Littel Childer Syng" from *There'll Always Be a Drayneflete*, by Osbert Lancaster, copyright, 1950, *The Atlantic Monthly*.

And to the artists who have signed their cartoons which they have permitted me to include.

Eric Posselt

Table of Contents

Alle Littel Childer Syng ii
OSBERT LANCASTER

Introduction ix
ERIC POSSELT

Crisp New Bills for Mr. Teagle 1
FRANK SULLIVAN

Merry Christmas in Ten Pieces 12
ROBERT M. YODER

A Christmas Spectacle 23
ROBERT BENCHLEY

The Same Old Christmas Story 33
HOLWORTH HALL

P.C.X.36 51
MAX BEERBOHM

Mr. Payson's Satirical Christmas 61
GEORGE ADE

Table of Contents

Dancing Dan's Christmas 73
DAMON RUNYON

Stephen Skarridge's Christmas 90
FRANK R. STOCKTON

Mr. Kaplan and the Magi 114
LEONARD Q. ROSS

The Worst Christmas Story 129
CHRISTOPHER MORLEY

The Errors of Santa Claus 146
STEPHEN LEACOCK

Ring Out, Wild Bells 154
D. B. WYNDHAM LEWIS

How Come Christmas? 161
ROARK BRADFORD

A Hint for Next Christmas 176
A. A. MILNE

Came the Dawn 179
J. A. BRILLAT-SAVARIN

Introduction

CONTRARY TO A WIDESPREAD BELIEF PARTICULARLY RAMP-
ant among anthologists, Charles Dickens did not in-
vent Christmas even though he did write more about it
than any other man, dead or alive, and in so doing un-
doubtedly contributed his share to the revival of its celebration in England and thus, indirectly, in the United States.
Considering the fact that in the year of Our Lord 1659,
Massachusetts passed a law reading, "Whoever shall be
found observing any such day as Christmas, or the like,
either by forebearing labor, or feasting any other way, shall
be fined five shillings," a law which remained in force for
fully twenty-two years; and considering that Christmas did
not become a legal holiday until late in the second half of
the Nineteenth Century, this is no mean achievement,
indeed.

Thus, the dictum avid researchers can locate in "Household Words"—where practically anything and everything
else can also be found—that Christmas is "a season of
greatness to some, of hilarity to many, and of importance

to all," assumes a significance quite out of proportion with other occasional banalities the great British humorist propounded in his day.

Granting the "importance to all"—particularly merchants, children, and fathers—and conceding that, as the day on which a stable in Bethlehem became the birthplace of a new era, Christmas is to millions the greatest day in recorded history, we are here concerned with Christmas as a season of hilarity.

In a world that has almost forgotten how to laugh, and actually has so deplorably little reason to laugh, this, too, seems of importance. And the editor verily believes that a Christmas anthology such as the present one, bringing together for the first time not merely the cream of the crop of humorous Christmas stories penned by some of the world's greatest writers, but also a selection of the best Christmas drawings, cartoons and illustrations by the finest artists of the last half century, is a worthy undertaking.

Of course, Rose Macauley, Dickens' estimable fellow worker in the vineyard of the word, anticipatorily put a damper on our enthusiasm by declaring that "Christmas books are a disease regularly contracted by publishers, literary editors and reviewers." But, then, she naturally did not know this volume, and probably thought of the tons of pretty white paper wasted on the usual sentimental pishposh wished on the public at a time when they are least suspicious and most apt to spend a stray dollar on, of all things, a book.

Let this, then, not dismay us, and let us uphold the belief that anything that helps people laugh and forget for a few moments the sorrows of the world, is in the truest Christian tradition.

Of course humor, to coin a phrase, is a funny thing, and what may seem the height of hilarity to one steeped in the tradition of "Punch" may very well produce nothing but a blank stare or, worse, a sneer on the part of one suckled at the bosom of "Puck," "Life," or the "New Yorker," and vice versa.

We can only hope that in view of the fact that we have, by the sweat of our brow, pored over the dusty volumes of not only these but dozens of other American, British and foreign language magazines, the fare here offered will seem rich and variegated enough to satisfy the most sybaritic selector.

The pictures, with very few exceptions, are, of course, not illustrations in the narrower sense of the word and belong to no specific story. An attempt has been made, however, to place them so that they either fit the spirit of a given tale or provide a pleasant shock by juxtaposition. In themselves they are as truly as the text both a mirror of our times and a reflection of the spirit of hilarity that, too, is Christmas.

My task is done and nothing is left me but to wish you all a merry, merry Christmas. But lest we be accused of being irreverent, let me quote, for the nonce, a few lines by Irwin Russel:

You bless us, please sah, eben if we're doin' wrong to-night;
Kase den we'll need de blessin' more'n ef we's doin' right;
An' let de blessin' stay wid us untel we come to die
An' goes to keep our Christmas wid dem sheriffs in de sky.

ERIC POSSELT

"Si-i-lent night!"

Crisp New Bills
for Mr. Teagle

FRANK SULLIVAN

COMING DOWN IN THE ELEVATOR, CLEMENT TEAGLE NO-
ticed an unwonted cordiality in Steve, the elevator boy,
and Harry, the doorman, but thought nothing of it until
he stopped at the bank on the corner to cash a check and
noticed the date.

December the twenty-fourth.

"Good gosh," Mr. Teagle thought, "I haven't bought a
present for Essie yet."

Then he remembered Steve and Harry.

His eye caught a legend on a Christmas placard on the wall. "It is more blessed to give than to receive," said the placard.

"Oh, yeah?" remarked Mr. Teagle, who, alas, was somewhat of a cynic.

Grumbling, he tore up the check he had started to write, and made out another, for a larger amount.

"Will you please give me new bills?" he asked.

"Indeed I shall," said Mr. Freyer, the teller, cordially.

He counted out one hundred dollars in new bills—crisp new bills—and passed them over to Mr. Teagle.

Then he tore up the check and handed the fragments to Mr. Teagle.

"Don't be alarmed, Mr. Teagle," said Mr. Freyer. "The bank of the Manhattan Company wants you to accept that one hundred dollars as a slight token of its esteem, with its best wishes for a Merry Christmas. You have been a loyal depositor here these many years. You have overdrawn fewer times than most of your fellow-depositors. You never argue about your monthly statements. You never feel insulted when a new teller identifies your signature before cashing your check. You are the kind of depositor who makes banking a joy, and I want to take this opportunity to tell you that we fellows around here, although we are not very demonstrative about that sort of thing, love you very much. A merry Christmas to you."

"You mean the bank is *giving* me this money?" said Mr. Teagle.

"That is the impression I was trying to convey," said Mr. Freyer, with a chuckle.

"Why—uh, thanks, Mr. Freyer. And—and thank the bank. This is—um—quite a surprise."

"Say no more about it, Mr. Teagle. And every Christmas joy to you, sir."

When Mr. Teagle left the bank he was somewhat perturbed, and a little stunned. He went back to the apartment to place the crisp new bills in envelopes for the boys, and as he left the elevator at his floor, Steve handed him an envelope.

"Merry Christmas, Mr. Teagle," said Steve.

"Thanks, Steve," said Mr. Teagle. "I'll—I'll be wishing you one a little later," he added significantly.

"You don't need to, Mr. Teagle," said Steve. "A man like you wishes the whole world a merry Christmas every day, just by living."

"Oh, Steve, damn nice of you to say that, but I'm sure it's not deserved," said Mr. Teagle, modestly struggling with a feeling that Steve spoke no more than the simple truth.

"Well, I guess we won't argue about *that*," said Steve, gazing affectionately at Mr. Teagle.

"I really believe that lad meant it," thought Mr. Teagle, as he let himself into the apartment. "I really believe he did."

Mr. Teagle opened the envelope Steve had handed him. A crisp new five-dollar bill fell out.

Downstairs in the lobby, a few minutes later, Steve was protesting.

"I tell you it wasn't a mistake, Mr. Teagle. I put the bill in there on purpose. For you."

"Steve, I couldn't take—"

"But you *can* take it, and you *will*, Mr. Teagle. And a very merry Christmas to you."

"Then you accept this, Steve, and a merry Christmas to *you*."

"Oh, no, Mr. Teagle. Not this year. You have been pretty swell to we fellows all the years you've lived here. Now it's our turn."

"You bet it is," said Harry the doorman, joining them and pressing a crisp new ten-dollar bill into Mr. Teagle's hand. "Merry Christmas, Mr. Teagle. Buy yourself something foolish with this. I only wish it could be more, but I've had rather a bad year in the market."

"I think the boys on the night-shift have a little surprise for Mr. Teagle, too," said Steve, with a twinkle in his eye.

Just then the superintendent came up.

"Well, well, well," he said jovially. "Who have we got here? Mr. Teagle, it may interest you to hear that I've been having a little chat about you with a certain old gentleman with a long, snowy beard and twinkling little eyes. Know who I mean?"

"Santa Claus?" Mr. Teagle asked.

"None other. And guess what! He asked me if you had been a good boy this year, and I was delighted to be able to tell him you had been, that you hadn't complained about the heat, hadn't run your radio after eleven at night, and hadn't had any late parties. Well, sir, you should have seen old Santa's face. He was tickled to hear it. Said he always knew you were a good boy. And what do you suppose he did?"

"What?" asked Mr. Teagle.

"He asked me to give you this and to tell you to buy yourself something for Christmas with it. Something foolish."

The super pressed a crisp new twenty-dollar bill upon Mr. Teagle.

"Merry Christmas, Mr. Teagle," said the super.

"Merry Christmas, Mr. Teagle," said Steve the elevator boy.

"Merry Christmas, Mr. Teagle," said Harry the doorman.

"Merry Christmas," said Mr. Teagle, in a voice you could scarcely hear. Remembering that he had to buy a present for Essie, he walked out, with the air of a bewildered gazelle. He was in a very, very puzzled state of mind as he walked down East Fifty-first Street, an agitation which did not subside when the proprietor of a cigar-store on Third Avenue rushed out, pressed a box of cigars on him, cried, "Merry Christmas, stranger!" and rushed back into his shop without another word.

To rush out of your store and give a box of cigars to a perfect stranger! And those boys at the apartment house! *And* the super!

Mr. Teagle thought of the many times he had grumbled

at being kept waiting a few minutes for the elevator or for a taxi. He felt ashamed. "By George," Mr. Teagle thought, "maybe Dickens was right."

Mr. Teagle approached the business of choosing a present for his wife in a far less carping spirit than was his Christmas wont.

"I'll get Essie something that'll knock her eye out," he thought. "She's a good old girl and she deserves a lot of credit for living with a grouch like me all these years. The best is none too good for her."

Suiting the action to the word, Mr. Teagle turned in at Cartier's and asked to see some square-cut emeralds. He selected one that could have done duty on a traffic light.

"I'm afraid I haven't the cash on me," he told the clerk. "I'll give you a check, and you can call the bank and verify—"

"That will not be necessary, sir," said the clerk, with a radiant smile. "You are Mr. Clement Teagle, I believe. In that case, Cartier wishes you to accept this trinket with the Christmas greetings of the firm. We are only sorry that you did not see fit to choose a diamond stomacher. Cartier will feel honored that one of its emeralds is adorning the finger of the wife of a man like Clement Teagle, a man four-square, a man who is a credit—All right, all right, all *right*, Mr. Teagle! Not another word, please. Cartier is adamant. You take this emerald or we may grow ugly about it. And don't lose it, sir, or I venture to say your good wife will give you Hail Columbia. Good day, sir, and God rest ye."

"Oh, dear! And we didn't get anything for <u>him</u>!"

Mr. Teagle found himself on the street. He accosted the first passer-by.

"Excuse me, stranger, but would you mind pinching me?"

"Certainly not, certainly not," said the stranger, cheerily. "There. Feel better?"

"Yes. Thank you very much," said Mr. Teagle.

"Here, buy yourself something for Christmas," said the stranger, pressing Mr. Teagle's hand. Mr. Teagle looked in the hand and found himself the possessor of a crisp new fifty-dollar bill.

At Fifth Avenue and Fifty-seventh Street, a Park & Tilford attendant rushed out and draped a huge basket, bedecked with ribbons and holly, on Mr. Teagle's arm.

"Everything drinkable for the Yuletide dinner, with love and kisses from Park & Tilford," whispered the clerk jovially. "Tell your wife to be sure and put the champagne in ice early, so it will be nice and cold."

"Oh, come on, come on," protested the butcher at Madison Avenue and Sixty-first Street. "Don't tell me you're too loaded down to carry a simple little turkey home, with the affectionate Christmas wishes of Shaffer's Market."

Mr. Shaffer laughed the rich laugh of the contented butcher.

"Don't take me too seriously when I say simple little turkey," he said. "That bird you got would make Roosevelt's Christmas turkey look like a humming bird. An undernourished humming bird. Pay for it? Certainly you won't pay for it! What do you take me for? It's Christmas. And you are Clement Teagle."

"Am I?" said Mr. Teagle, humbly.

Long before he reached home, Mr. Teagle had had such a plethora of gifts pressed upon him by friendly strangers that there was nothing to do but load them into a taxicab. And Mr. Teagle was not quite as surprised as he might have been earlier in the day when the driver refused to accept any money, but grinned and said: "Let's just charge this trip to good old St. Nick."

"Why, Clem!" said Mrs. Teagle, when, with the aid of the entire house staff, Mr. Teagle had deposited his gifts in the dining room. "Why, Clem, I already *bought* a turkey! Clem, you've been drinking."

"I have *not!*" Mr. Teagle shouted.

"Well, don't get on your high horse," said Mrs. Teagle. "It's Christmas Eve. I don't mind. Only—you know your stomach. And you do look funny."

"I may look funny, but I have not been drinking," Mr. Teagle insisted. "Look! H-h-h-h-h-h."

His breath was as the new-mown hay.

"See what I got you for Christmas, Essie." Mrs. Teagle opened the jewel-case and the emerald gleamed up at her. It was a moment before she could speak.

"No, Clem," she said. "You work too hard for your money. I don't deserve this. I won't take it from you. You've been too good to me as it is. I don't want any Christmas present from you, dear. I want to *give* you one—and oh, by the way, Clem, before I forget it, the funniest thing happened this afternoon. The income-tax man was here, the federal income-tax man. Said he just dropped in to wish you a merry Christmas. He left this check for your entire last year's income tax. He said the Government wants to give it back to you as a token of affection and in recognition of your many superb qualities as a citizen and—oh, I can't remember everything he said, but he made quite a flowery speech about you, dear—Why, Clem, what's the matter?"

Mr. Teagle had burst into tears.

"A merry Christmas, Essie," he said, through his sobs, and, in the language of Tiny Tim, " 'God bless us every one.' "

11

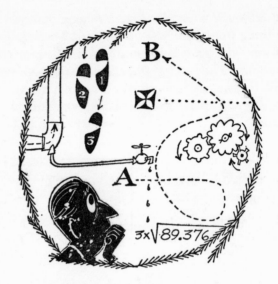

Merry Christmas
in Ten Pieces

ROBERT M. YODER

*Yes, Virginia, there is a Santa Claus, and he has a home
up near the North Pole, where it is colder than a bathroom
floor. But don't believe that story about his having a lot of
little dwarfs who put toys together for him, singing as they
hammer. Nobody puts toys together, until Christmas Eve.
Toys come in sixteen pieces, with one missing, and are put
together by a large band of Involuntary Elves who call ourselves Santa's Press-Gang Helpers. We don't exactly sing,*

*either, although a certain low, ominous murmur can be
heard rising from a million homes on Christmas Eve. Put
it this way, kid: That ain't no dwarf; that's your old man,
beaten down. The luckless peon bought the toys; now he is
learning that he has to finish manufacturing them, too, and
by one* A.M. *his mood will make Scrooge seem like Sunny
Ebenezer.*

THE FIRST THING YOUR FRIGHTENED EYE LIGHTS ON, IN
the store, is a nice little red wagon, and you think, in
your fatuous adult way, that this is just the thing to
brighten the young heart. If you weren't partially paralyzed
by the fear that you are shopping too late, you would
realize that if the kid wants a wagon at all, it isn't this
chaste little model. He would want one twice this size, with
demountable tires, a ram-jet engine, electric lights, an over-
drive and a windshield wiper, at $79.75. The kid next door
has had one like that for two years and uses it only to haul
his good toys in. Then you see the rocket-firing antiaircraft
gun and realize that this is the answer. While it will not do
bodily harm, and is therefore a partial bust to start with, it
is a realistic-looking little number, and you buy it, at an ex-
ceedingly realistic price.

About the hour on Christmas Eve when you are in mild
shock for fear the thing won't arrive, the delivery man stum-
bles in with a large package that can't be anything else.
Will you put it under the tree that way? Or will you have
it out in the open, so the child may see this splendid sight
first thing in the morning? Full of Christmas sentiment,
you decide to expose the gun to full, gladsome view. So you

14

tear off the wrapping. Here is a dial, here is a leg, here is a muzzle. You thought it would look like the model in the store, did you? Well, Santa has a little surprise for you. It's in pieces, and you are going to have to put it together. Merry Christmas, in at least ten pieces.

There is a sheet or folder of directions which could not get under your skin worse if they were in Spanish. They are written in the special language of directions, a mechanical gobbledegook achieved by writing the directions first in Ruthenian and then allowing the translation to curdle. A stop sign from the same mumbling pen would take 200 words. In the language of directions, "close the door" would read like this: "Grasp door-opening device with right knob-grasper and exert pressure outward until Panel A fills Aperture B. If scream is heard, other hand may be caught in opening." Along with being as turgid as possible, the directions are printed in a miniature type face known as Myopia Old Style, which is two sizes smaller than pearl and is otherwise used only to print the Declaration of Independence on souvenir pennies.

Well, lying there in pieces, the gun looks like nothing at all; it's got to be assembled. The first line you encounter in the directions says: "Using ring grasper from Assembly Kit, grasp collector ring near tube spar tightening guide rod" . . . but, thank heaven, that goes with some other toy. Your own directions start out more simply: "Connect round opening at end of Feeder Spring A with hooked end of trigger lock restraining bar by placing round opening over hook and pressing." What'd he think you'd do—spot-weld it? (The answer, unfortunately, is that he expects more than that, but not just yet.) Now the guy begins getting esoteric.

"If retaining mechanism fails to admit trigger, horizontal opening of drum impeding stopper should be widened horizontally." He means if the damned trigger won't go into the guard, you got to cut more room, and sure enough, it won't. This is going to be the only gun in the neighborhood with a demountable (falling out) trigger, unless you fix it. If retaining mechanism fails to admit what it's supposed to retain, then it should never have left the factory, but it's too late for that kind of recrimination now. Getting a hammer from the basement, a good paring knife and a screw driver, you manage to make the trigger go where it should, with one very bad moment when you think you've split the thing.

Well, the barrel, H, slides into place nicely; maybe things are beginning to go your way. The next step is to fit Firing Platform Z on Tripod, the Tripod being made by inserting Metal-tipped Ends of Legs into Sockets, which is child's play. Now all it takes is two bolts, L and M, which you slip into place with great efficiency. They must be firmly in place, the directions say, or gun will not swivel on Platform Z; you might say, it won't swivel on any platform. A neat little bag contained the bolts, and in it you find the nut for Bolt L. But half an hour later you are still rummaging through wrapping paper in a grim search for the other nut, the crucial nut, the nut without which, as the Latins say, nothing. You may have 128 nuts of assorted sizes in a jar in the basement, but you will not have one that fits Bolt M.

That is a freak size used nowhere else in the whole panoply of American industry. It is part of a shipment the toy manufacturer bought up from the Uruguayan War Assets Administration.

It is 11:45 by the time you manage to make the bolt hold with a piece of wire wrapped around it, and if the kid looks at that part, he will feel sure this toy is something the fireman repainted for the poor. Meanwhile the house has grown cold, three of the Christmas-tree lights have winked at you by burning out, and your cigarette has fallen out of the ash tray and burned a six-dollar hole in the carpet. But the gun is starting to look like a weapon, and there can't be much more—only a couple of odd-looking metal pieces are left and a cardboard circle marked "Cosmic Ray Computer Dial."

One of the pieces of metal is easy enough to use. It's the missing plug, for lack of which the barrel has had that tendency to point to the floor like the tail of a whipped hound. The other is the crank with which the young gunner moves the barrel to keep on his target. You tackle the easiest job first—the computer is nothing more than two sections of light cardboard. "Bending Tabs A, C, E and G," the directions say, "fit them into Slots B, D, F and H." The cardboard is a special kind which is as stiff as metal for a minute and then relaxes completely as you push, so that in twenty minutes you have four dog-eared tabs holding one crumpled dial marked with a little blood from the finger you cut trying to enlarge the slots.

Now you reach the part of the directions that tell you

The compliments of the season.

to fix on the telescopic sight. The diagram shows a handsome metal gadget coming to a square end, fitted into a ring fastened neatly around the end of the barrel. The only piece of metal you have left, outside of the crank, is a cotter pin. Even if you had missing part R, you still would have nothing like missing part Q which fits into it. You ransack the wrapping paper again, in what the novelists call cold fury, but with no luck. Finally, with great self-control, you smooth the wrinkled directions and read that jargon over again out loud. It is then that you come across Step 2. "In assembling Model A-100 Junior, our second-rate cheaper model for pikers, Step 1 may be disregarded," the directions say. "No sight comes with this model. There is, however, a cotter pin. You can stick it on the barrel with adhesive tape and play like it's a sight. It ain't much, but neither are you."

There is one final step—mounting the crank. "Slip Directional Crank 16 through Arm Y into Slot EE," the directions say. "When in position, give crank one quarter turn counterclockwise. Trigger should then fall sharply back into firing position." This is simplicity itself, and the only trouble is that if the crank goes through Arm Y, it misses Slot EE by a good quarter of an inch. The bitter thoughts that arise on Christmas Eve about the sleepwalker who bored that slot must visibly affect the temperature.

But the direction writer thought about this impasse, forehanded soul that he is. "It may be necessary, for best results"—meaning, to make the thing work at all—"to enlarge aperture in Arm Y. This can be done quickly and easily by using a 16.3 metal file without tang, a 13-oz. ding-

ing hammer, and some Australian-canoe-builders' flux."
This is equipment the ordinary household would be just
as likely to have as a Javanese blowgun and a guroo bird,
and you know, as your thoughts profane the early Christmas air, that the only 16.3 file in the world is one resting in
the manufacturer's plant 850.3 miles away across the snowy
landscape. So you gouge out a new Slot EE four times the
proper size, the crank falls into place, wobbling foolishly,
and the task is done. If it holds together until Christmas
afternoon, you will be agreeably surprised, and a glance at
the clock tells you that won't be long.

*Yes, Virginia, there is a Santa Claus. If there weren't, ugly
mobs of maddened parents would rove the streets Christmas Day armed with bolts, pins, wheels and axles, and some
toy manufacturer would end up assembled on Movable Rail
A wearing Feathers B and Tar C, after a slight going-over
with No. 16 emery paper and a common hydraulic half-
knurled center punch.*

"She started flapping them—and they worked!"

"Now remember, even if one or two members of the audience fail to applaud, you are NOT to stick out your tongues at them!"

A Christmas Spectacle

ROBERT BENCHLEY

AT THE OPENING OF THE ENTERTAINMENT THE SUPERIN-
tendent will step into the footlights, recover his balance apologetically, and say:

"Boys and girls of the Intermediate Department, parents
and friends: I suppose you all know why we are here to-
night. (At this point the audience will titter apprehen-
sively.) Mrs. Drury and her class of little girls have been

(*Reprinted from Collier's by permission.*)

24

working very hard to make this entertainment a success, and I am sure that everyone here tonight is going to have what I overheard one of my boys the other day calling 'some good time.' (Indulgent laughter from the little boys.) And may I add before the curtain goes up that immediately after the entertainment we want you all to file out into the Christian Endeavor room, where there will be a Christmas tree, 'with all the fixin's,' as the boys say." (Shrill whistling from the little boys and immoderate applause from everyone.)

There will then be a wait of twenty-five minutes, while sounds of hammering and dropping may be heard from behind the curtains. The Boys' Club orchestra will render the "Poet and Peasant Overture" four times in succession, each time differently.

At last one of the curtains will be drawn back; the other will catch on something and have to be released by hand; someone will whisper loudly, "Put out the lights," following which the entire house will be plunged into darkness. Amid catcalls from the little boys, the footlights will at last go on, disclosing:

The windows in the rear of the vestry rather ineffectively concealed by a group of small fir trees on standards, one of which has already fallen over, leaving exposed a corner of the map of Palestine and the list of gold-star classes for November. In the center of the stage is a larger tree, undecorated, while at the extreme left, invisible to everyone in the audience except those sitting at the extreme right, is an imitation fireplace, leaning against the wall.

Twenty-five seconds too early little Flora Rochester will prance out from the wings, uttering the first shrill notes of a song, and will have to be grabbed by eager hands and pulled back. Twenty-five seconds later the piano will begin "The Return of the Reindeer" with a powerful accent on the first note of each bar, and Flora Rochester, Lillian McNulty, Gertrude Hamingham and Martha Wrist will swirl on, dressed in white, and advance heavily into the footlights, which will go out.

There will then be an interlude while Mr. Neff, the sexton, adjusts the connection, during which the four little girls stand undecided whether to brave it out or cry. As a compromise they giggle and are herded back into the wings by Mrs. Drury, amid applause. When the lights go on again, the applause becomes deafening, and as Mr. Neff walks triumphantly away, the little boys in the audience will whistle: "There she goes, there she goes, all dressed up in her Sunday clothes!"

"The Return of the Reindeer" will be started again and the showgirls will reappear, this time more gingerly and somewhat dispirited. They will, however, sing the following, to the music of the "Ballet Pizzicato" from "Sylvia":

> "We greet you, we greet you,
> On this Christmas Eve so fine.
> We greet you, we greet you,
> And wish you a good time."

They will then turn toward the tree and Flora Rochester will advance, hanging a silver star on one of the branches,

"On stage, Angels!"

(Reprinted from Collier's by permission.)

meanwhile reciting a verse, the only distinguishable words of which are: "I am Faith so strong and pure—"

At the conclusion of the recitation, the star will fall off.

Lillian McNulty will then step forward and hang her star on a branch, reading her lines in clear tones:

> "And I am Hope, a virtue great,
>   My gift to Christmas now I make,
>   That children and grown-ups may hope today
>   That tomorrow will be a merry Christmas Day."

The hanging of the third star will be consummated by Gertrude Hamingham, who will get as far as "Sweet Charity I bring to place upon the tree—" at which point the strain will become too great and she will forget the remainder. After several frantic glances toward the wings, from which Mrs. Drury is sending out whispered messages to the effect that the next line begins, "My message bright—" Gertrude will disappear, crying softly.

After the morale of the cast has been in some measure restored by the pianist, who, with great presence of mind, plays a few bars of "Will There Be Any Stars In My Crown?" to cover up Gertrude's exit, Martha Wrist will unleash a rope of silver tinsel from the foot of the tree, and, stringing it over the boughs as she skips around in a circle, will say, with great assurance:

> " 'Round and 'round the tree I go,
>   Through the holly and the snow
>   Bringing love and Christmas cheer
>   Through the happy year to come."

"My mommy took me to see Santa Claus yesterday.
I sat on his lap and gave him my autograph"

(Reprinted from Collier's by permission.)

At this point there will be a great commotion and the jangling of sleigh-bells off stage, and Mr. Creamer, rather poorly disguised as Santa Claus, will emerge from the opening in the imitation fireplace. A great popular demonstration for Mr. Creamer will follow. He will then advance to the footlights, and, rubbing his pillow and ducking his knees to denote joviality, will say thickly through his false beard:

"Well, well, well, what have we here? A lot of bad little boys and girls who aren't going to get any Christmas presents this year? (Nervous laughter from the little boys and girls.) Let me see! Let me see! I have a note here from Dr. Whidden. Let's see what it says. (Reads from a paper on which there is obviously nothing written.) 'If you and the young people of the Intermediate Department will come into the Christian Endeavor room, I think we may have a little surprise for you . . .' Well, well, well! What do you suppose it can be? (Cries of 'I know, I know!' from sophisticated ones in the audience.) Maybe it is a bottle of castor-oil! (Raucous jeers from the little boys and elaborately simulated disgust on the part of the little girls.) Well, anyway, suppose we go out and see? Now if Miss Liftnagle will oblige us with a little march on the piano, we will all form in single file—"

At this point there will ensue a stampede toward the Christian Endeavor room, in which chairs will be broken, decorations demolished, and the protesting Mr. Creamer badly hurt.

This will bring to a close the first part of the entertainment.

The Conjuror's Christmas

31

Why Should the Little Kids Have All the Fun?

The Same Old
Christmas Story

HOLWORTH HALL

I T WAS CHRISTMAS EVE IN THE TRENCHES OF THE ARGONNE
and the Marne. Fortunately for the sake of your emo-
tions, however, the scene of the present dramatic interlude
is laid in the trenches of neither the Marne nor the
Argonne. For that matter, it was also Christmas Eve in the
trenches of the Broadway subway, and the twenty-second
of December in Philadelphia.

In the bay-window of the exclusive Seaview Golf Club on the corner of Fourth and Fifth Avenues, Harrington Hetherington sat staring moodily out at the softly falling snow. He was a clean-limbed specimen of American manhood. In attire he was the apotheosis of Vanity Fair; and in physiognomy he was not unlike Mrs. Vernon Castle. His attitude was that of Rodin's "Thinker," and his clothes were made by Lucile.

He was practically alone in the club. Everyone else had gone to spend Christmas out-of-town—everyone but Harrington Hetherington. And as the afternoon wore steadily into dusk, or occasionally reversed, and dashed steadily back toward sunrise, Hetherington relapsed into deeper and deeper melancholy. He had no family. He had no relations. He had no friends. He had no creditors. In all the world, there was no one to seek him out. He had nowhere to go for Christmas. Accordingly, as he slumped into the innermost recesses of his chair, his thoughts unerringly turned to an incident of his youth.

At the age of nineteen he had run away from his home in Newark. He had left behind him a beautful girl who loved him. It was his intention to accumulate a fortune, and to marry her. For years they had corresponded fatuously. He had sent her gifts and tokens of his adoration. When he was twenty-one, he sent her a leather pillow-cover with an Indian head on it, and fringe around the outskirts. When he was twenty-six he sent her a hand-made copy of a Gibson drawing, passepartouted. When he was thirty, he sent her a picture-postcard of Trinity Church. When he was thirty-five, he sent her an automobile pennant from Schenectady, with a message of love in code. The words read, "Excuse my dust," but he knew that she would understand. The eyes of love cannot be deceived.

But eventually they ceased to correspond. He was now a wealthy clubman, and he had forgotten the beautiful girl of his youth. He had forgotten many other things. Among them, he had forgotten that his father had spelled the good old surname "Hetherington" in a curious way. He had spelled it: "H-i-g-g-i-n-s."

As he sat in the exclusive club, and stared out at the kaleidoscopic splendor of varicolored decorations, and the display of March magazines on the brilliantly lighted news-stands, Hetherington thought again of his youth. His conscience gnawed him, and at first he belligerently gnawed back, but at length his braggadocio failed him, and he suffered violently. First, with symptoms of frightful agony, he kindled a cigar, and suffered like that for some time. Later, he swallowed a cooling draught, and found balm for his soul in the awful torment. Little by little the solitude of the club weighed upon him; he could endure it no longer. He rang for a boy. There was no response. He rang the cocktail-gong. Still there was no response. Then he pulled the whistle cord.

A youth hurried into the room and stood trembling.

"What's the matter with you?" demanded Hetherington roughly. "What's the matter with the service in this club? I've got a good notion to report you to the manager— What's your number? Well, 365, you ought to be fired, and

you know it. . . . Shaking dice out behind the grill, I suppose!"

The well-trained boy stepped to one side so as not to
tremble on the priceless rugs.

"N-no, sir," he faltered. "I . . . I was writing . . ."
Hetherington guffawed exclusively.

"To Santa Claus, of course," he said with biting sarcasm.
The boy snarled viciously and showed his teeth.

"Y-yes, sir."

"What! What's that? You don't mean to tell me . . .
oh, look here, 365, don't try *that* excuse! You don't think
I'm simple enough to think *you* believe in Santa Claus!"

"Oh, no, sir—I don't—but—"

"Well?"

The boy reddened, thrusting his shoulders forward so as
to look like Leach Cross.

"It's my little brother and sisters—"

"Go on."

"Well—*they* believe in Santa Claus . . . and, . . .
and they write letters to him, to hang up with their stockings—"

"Is that any reason for *you* to write letters—and let me
ring three times? Is it?"

"Why, you see . . . if I didn't write a letter, too, and
hang it up—they'd think it was queer—and they'd ask questions—and maybe they'd find out—"

"Oh! *Now* I get it—you *want* 'em to keep on believing
all that rot?"

"Yes, sir."

"Well, what did you ask Santa Claus for?"

"A few little things . . . you know how it is, sir . . . the kids wouldn't understand if I asked for what I really do want . . . so I asked for some new handkerchiefs and things like that. . . ."

"Expect to get 'em?"

"Yes, sir."

"Oh, then you *do* believe—"

"Why, sir, it's this way . . . in my house there's just my mother and the kids . . . I'm the only one that's old enough to work. . . . I know I'll get what I asked for, because I took jolly good care to ask for what I know I'm going to get; and the kids'll get what *they* asked for, if things don't cost too much, because . . . I'm Santa Claus!"

Hetherington gave a Fifth Avenue laugh,—long and rich.

"I'll be hanged if you look it! . . . Well, St. Nick, what do you *really* want?"

"What I really want," said the boy almost audibly, "is for my mother to be happy again. . . . I can't ask Santa for that, can I?"

"No," said the wealthy clubman thoughtfully, "I'm afraid you can't. Well—hurry up and bring me a mint julep. Christmas! Tomfoolishness! Anyway . . . let's have a bit of local color. Tell the bartender to put evergreen in it instead of mint."

Left alone, he regarded the ceiling earnestly. "Perfect twaddle, this Christmas idiocy . . . and yet . . . when you come to think of it, it *is* hard on the poor little brats in the tenements. It wouldn't take much to make them happy . . . a few minutes; a few dollars. . . ."

He rose, and went diffidently to the manager's office, and attracted his attention by poking him in the midriff with a malacca cane.

"I want to get some information about 365," he said. "What's his salary?"

"Salary, Mr. Hetherington? Why, the new boys get five dollars a month to start."

"Five dollars? . . . Well, that's pretty high. That's the interest on $36,500 for one day. That's a lot. I rather thought they weren't paid that much. Still—"

"If you want to make a complaint—"

Hetherington struck him across the face with his gloves, and threw the gloves into the coal-hod.

"Complaint? Who said anything about a complaint? When I want to make a complaint, you'll know it fast enough! I want to find out where he lives!"

"Yes, sir," said the manager hastily. "Just a second, sir."

II

In a humble tenement on Riverside Drive a very large widow sat surrounded by four starving children. Two of them were starving at the top of their lungs. The apartment was bare, cheerless and sordid to the point of squalor. It held no furniture—nothing but floor. The radiator was only lukewarm, and hardly tempered the chill which struck deep to the bone, and deeper to the heart.

39

In their innocent faith, the children had already hung to the jigsawed mantel their stockings, with form letters attached . . . The youngest girl, who had no stockings, had hung up a union suit. All of them hoped, prayed, believed that Santa Claus would come down the steam pipes, and leave them the simple gifts they craved. And such simple gifts! A doll, a book, and candy for Rosamond; a Teddy bear, a book, and candy for Gwendolyn; a baseball, an air rifle, and a dark lantern for Percival; a Rolls Royce for Ike.

The widow herself was diligently embroidering a canvas derrick-cover, by the faint glimmer of a flaming arc light, which was the sole illumination of the tiny room.

"Mother," said Rosamond, "are you *sure* he'll come? What odds are you giving?"

"Don't you know?" said Ike wrapping the morning *Tribune* around a warm brick.

"I don't believe there's any Santa Claus," said Gwendolyn stoutly. "I'll take the short end of twenty to one on it."

"What! Oooh! The thing you said!" They glared at her in speechless horror.

"Well, I don't! Who ever seen him? Jever know *anybody* that seen him? Then how jer know there *is* a Santa Claus?"

"Jever see your brains?" retorted Percival. "Then how do you know—"

"Mother, it ain't so! Is it? So now!"

"She's a naughty, bad girl, she is! I guess if he heard *that* he'd stay away, all right!"

"Mother, I'm hungry!"

"Hush, dear," implored the widow gently. "Be patient,

my darlings. We shall soon have food again, say by the middle of February. Ah, if Harrington Hetherington, the rich derrick-maker only knew how we suffer! I scarcely weigh two hundred and fifty now—and when I was young and healthy— But come! . . . it's time you were all asleep."

Even under the thin blankets on the thickest part of the floor, the four little children shivered pitiably.

"Mother . . . we're cold!"

Skilled by long experience in the makeshifts of poverty, she took the front door off the hinges, and laid it gently over them. At length they slept; the lines of pain faded from their little faces, to be replaced by the smiles of pleasant dreams.

With a bitter sigh, the widow resumed her task. Then startlingly, a pair of arms went around her neck; she looked up into the eyes of her boy Reginald, who worked at the Seaview Golf Club.

"Dear mother," he said, as he kissed her without removing the Fatima from his mouth, "haven't you finished yet?"

"No, dear . . . and I must have this done, and get my pay, or the landlord . . ." She shuddered as she brushed the hot ashes from her lips.

"Mother, have you *always* got to do such hard work? Isn't there anything easier, or anything that will pay you better? Great Heaven, is there no moral justice in all this city?"

"No," she said brokenly, "not one." Tears welled to her

eyes, but she wiped them quickly away, for she had taken up the embroidered canvas derrick-cover once more, and feared lest the drops should fall upon and injure the delicate fabric.

"Well . . . what did the babies ask for?"

"See for yourself," she said. "Reginald, it breaks my heart. . . ."

The boy turned from the childish scrawls attached to the Holeproofs.

"I know . . . the worst of it is that they'll have to be disappointed . . ."

"I was afraid of that, dear boy—"

"I've got two dollars; and there's Pol Roger to buy, and oatmeal. . . . I don't see . . ." He clenched his puny fists, and laughed villainously, as in the third act. "Oh, what's the difference?" he said. "Suppose we *are* hungry the day after—we're used to it! But to be hungry in the soul on Christmas! *No!* Those kids are going to have what they want!"

"Reginald! Listen, dear! You mustn't . . . it's the rent, too . . . you mustn't! You're not Creosote—"

He paused in the doorway and gave the Chihuahua salute.

"No, mother," he said quietly. "But to the kids I'm something better yet—I'm Santa Claus!"

III

Hetherington looked at the clock. It was a typical club clock. It struck nine, and since the hands were pointing to twenty-seven minutes of four, that proved that it was exactly nineteen minutes past ten. It was time!

He ordered a taxicab; to his amazement there were none to be obtained. Even the chauffeurs, it seemed, were celebrating. He ordered a motor truck—they were all engaged. Dauntless, he set out on foot. He fought the storm to the shopping district. A United Cigar store yet remained open . . . recklessly he ordered whatever suggested itself to his untutored imagination. Toys and dolls, a drum, candy, books, flowers, a dark-lantern, a Teddy bear, an air-rifle, handkerchiefs, a Rolls-Royce, a turkey, vegetables . . . the complete order was stupendous.

"Send them," he directed, "to 9870 Riverside—"

"Sorry, sir. The last delivery has gone."

"*Gone!*"

"Yes, sir. Gone."

He looked at the enormous pile, and for a moment he wavered. You could have seen him do it.

"No—they *shall* not be disappointed! Wrap them carefully, my good man, in a small, compact package—I'll carry them myself!"

Twenty minutes later, burdened almost beyond his immense strength, he faced the storm once more. The street was slippery with thousands of dollars worth of ice, but he staggered courageously onward. He fell frequently, breaking something nearly every time. Once it was a soda-biscuit; once it was the drum-head; once it was a couple of legs; but still he staggered on. His ears were frost-bitten; his arms ached fearfully; his vegetables were frozen solid; but still he staggered on; until at last, several hours after he had reached the absolute limit of his endurance, he saw the lights of the Drive twinkling fitfully before him, and knew that his journey was at an end.

He reached the house; he stumbled into the hallway. He staggered up one flight. Two flights. Three flights. Four flights. Five flights. Six flights. Seven flights. Eight flights. Nine flights. Then he thought to ask where the widow lived. They said it was on the second floor.

He gained the landing. The door was gone; but he didn't notice it. His mood was above such things. He knocked on the place where the door ought to be and went in. As he stood in the embrasure, coated with snow, weighted down by bundles tied with holly tape, the widow stared at him keenly . . . recoiled . . . screamed . . . and prepared to faint.

The children lifted sleepy heads; all at once they scrambled from the bed, and leaped towards him.

"Santa Claus!" they shrieked in mad triumph. "Santa Claus!" Hetherington went down under the numbing crash of a sand-bag on his occipital bone; four wild captors pounced upon his chest.

"Hurray!" shouted Gwendolyn. "Hit him with the brick in the *Tribune*, Percy! It's Santa Claus *and we've got him!*"

IV

When he was on his feet, shaken, indignant, he perceived that the widow was leaning breathless against several of the walls. One hand clutched at her breast; the others moved spasmodically towards him.

"Robert!" she choked. "Robert!"

Hetherington reeled dizzily.

"Clarice . . . you . . ."

"It ain't Robert . . . it's Santa Claus!" wailed Rosamond, clinging to his coat-tails. He kicked her off.

"They said you were dead, Robert . . . they showed me a certificate from a mortuary establishment . . . we never heard from you . . . they forced me to marry against my will . . ."

"Them papers was forged! I . . . I came here to make my fortune . . . when I wrote home, they said you were married . . . life has been more or less nothing to me since. . . ."

"I thought you hadn't cared . . ."

"Cared! I loved you! And you have been . . . here!"

"When Himself died, Himself left nothing . . . I have had to support my babies . . . I am an embroiderer for the Derrick-Cover Company—"

He paled, and put a hand to his throat, and throttled himself.

"Oh . . . the irony of it!" he gasped, tearing himself loose—"It . . . it can't be true! Oh, the pity of it! Clarice . . . it was with that company that I first found work . . . and now I'm the president of it . . . the largest stockholder . . . I'm Harrington Hetherington!".

She smiled weakly.

"So—you changed your name, too! That explains all. It

wouldn't have been so hard, Robert, if I could have remembered . . . or dreamed . . . that somewhere you were still living . . . and thinking of me . . . and for the last nineteen years I've had a warrant out for you for breach of promise, and a civil summons for you on account of the sixty dollars you borrowed from Dad the day you left."

He went swiftly to her, and took her in his arms.

"Dearest," he whispered, "you're free now . . . is it too late for me to make amends? Can't I atone for the past? Can't I Clarice?"

"What a funny Santa Claus!" said Isaac to Gwendolyn, as they opened another package, and extracted the trading stamps. "He's kissing mother . . . isn't it funny? His nerve is all right—but what do you think of his taste!"

V

The churchbells chimed the hour of midnight. Reginald, bearing three or four small parcels, came noiselessly into the room, and halted, spellbound. Hetherington, his arm nearly all the way around the widow, sat on the floor, surrounded by toys and laughing children. A Christmas tree stood in the corner. A magnificent fire rattled in the radiator. Food was burning on the stove. A bucket of gold eagles hung on the gas-jet.

"Mr. Hetherington!" The boy's hand went up in salute. "Yes, sir," he said automatically. "Rye high, sir."

The wealthy clubman laughed gleefully.

"Come in, old fellow . . . come on in, St. Nick! Sometimes we get what we ask for after all! Bless you, my boy

. . . you don't know what you've done for us! You're going to be my boy . . . do you know that? And you're going to college; and your brothers and sisters are going to be educated, whether they like it or not; you're all coming to live with me and be rich and unscrupulous . . . come on in, 365, this time *I'm* Santa Claus . . . and it's Christmas!"

Peace on earth; good form among gentlemen.

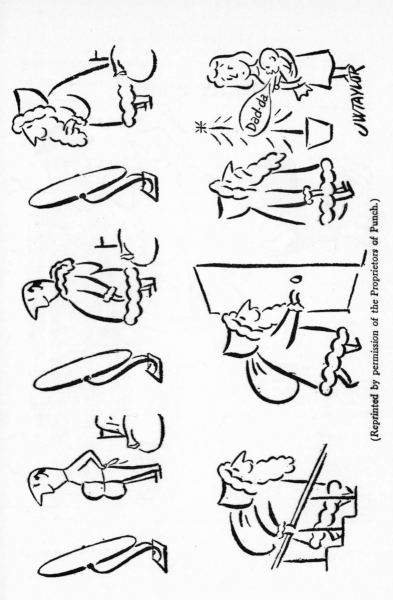

(Reprinted by permission of the Proprietors of Punch.)

49

"Do you mind if I walk beside you a while? They won't
throw them at you."

P.C.X. 36

(In the Manner of Rudyard Kipling)

MAX BEERBOHM

Then it's collar 'im tight,
In the name o' the Lawd!
'Ustle 'im, shake 'im till 'e's sick!
Wot, 'e would, would 'e? Well,
Then yer've got ter give 'im 'Ell,
An' it's trunch, trunch, truncheon does the trick.

Police Station Ditties

I HAD SPENT CHRISTMAS EVE AT THE CLUB, LISTENING TO
a grand pow-wow between certain of the choicer sons
of Adam. Then Slushby had cut in. Slushby is one who
writes to newspapers and is theirs obediently "HUMANI-
TARIAN." When Slushby cuts in, men remember they
have to be up early next morning.

Sharp round a corner on the way home, I collided with
something firmer than the regulation pillar-box. I righted
myself after the recoil and saw some stars that were very
pretty indeed. Then I perceived the nature of the obstruc-
tion.

"Evening, Judlip," I said sweetly, when I had collected
my hat from the gutter. "Have I broken the law, Judlip?
If so, I'll go quiet."

" 'Time yer was in bed," grunted X. 36. "Yer Ma'll be
lookin' out for yer."

This from the friend of my bosom! It hurt. Many were
the nightbeats I had been privileged to walk with Judlip,
imbibing curious lore that made glad the civilian heart of
me. Seven whole 8 by 5 inch note-books had I pitmanised
to the brim with Judlip. And now to be repulsed as one of
the uninitiated! It hurt horrid.

There is a thing called Dignity. Small boys sometimes
stand on it. Then they have to be kicked. Then they get
down, weeping. I don't stand on Dignity.

"What's wrong, Judlip?" I asked, more sweetly than
ever. "Drawn a blank to-night?"

"Yuss. Drawn a blank blank blank. 'Avent 'ad so much

as a kick at a lorst dog. Christmas Eve ain't what it was."
I felt for my note-book. "Lawd! I remember the time when
the drunks and disorderlies down this street was as thick as
flies on fly-paper. One just picked 'em orf with one's finger
and thumb. A bloomin' battew, that's wot it wos."

"The night's yet young, Judlip," I insinuated with a jerk
of my thumb at the flaring windows of the "Rat and Blood
Hound." At that moment the saloon-door swung open,
emitting a man and woman who walked with linked arms
and exceeding great care.

Judlip eyed them longingly as they tacked up the street.
Then he sighed. Now, when Judlip sighs the sound is like
unto that which issues from the vent of a Crosby boiler
when the cock-gauges are at 260° F.

"Come, Judlip!" I said. "Possess your soul in patience.
You'll soon find someone to make an example of. Meanwhile"—I threw back my head and smacked my lips—"the
usual, Judlip?"

In another minute I emerged through the swing-door,
bearing a furtive glass of that same "usual," and nipped
down the mews where my friend was wont to await these
little tokens of esteem.

"To the Majesty of the Law, Judlip!"

When he had honoured the toast, I scooted back with
the glass, leaving him wiping the beads of his beard-bristles.
He was in his philosophic mood when I rejoined him at
the corner.

"Wot am I?" he said, as we paced along. "A bloomin'
cypher. Wot's the Serjint? 'E's got the Inspector over 'im.

53

Over above the Inspector there's the Sooprintendent. Over above 'im's the old red-tape-masticatin' Yard. Over above than there's the 'Ome Sec. Wot's 'e? A cypher, like me. Why?" Judlip looked up at the stars. "Over above 'im's We Dunno Wot. Somethin' wot issues its horders an' regulations an' divisional injunctions, inscrootable like, but p'repmtory; an' we 'as ter see as 'ow they're carried out, not arskin' no questions, but each man goin' about 'is dooty."

"'Is dooty,'" said I, looking up from my note-book. "Yes, I've got that."

"Life ain't a bean-feast. It's a 'arsh reality. An' them as makes it a bean-feast 'as got to be 'arshly dealt with accordin'. That's wot the Force is put 'ere for from Above. Not as 'ow we ain't fallible. We makes our mistakes. An' when we makes 'em we sticks to 'em. For the honour o' the Force. Which same is the jool Britannia wears on 'er bosom as a charm against hanarchy. That's wot the brarsted old Beaks don't understand. Yer remember Smithers of our Div?"

I remembered Smithers—well. As fine, upstanding, square-toed, bullet-headed, clean-living a son of a gun as ever perjured himself in the box. There was nothing of the softy about Smithers. I took off my billicock to Smithers' memory.

"Sacrificed to public opinion? Yuss," said Judlip, pausing at a front door and flashing his 45 c.p. down the slot of a two-grade Yale. "Sacrificed to a parcel of creamin' old women wot ort ter 'ave gorn down on their knees an' thanked Gawd for such a protector. 'E'll be out in another 'alf year. Wot'll 'e do then, pore devil? Go a bust on 'is conduc' money an' throw in 'is lot with them same hexperts wot 'ad a 'oly terror of 'im." Then Judlip swore gently.

"What should you do, O Great One, if ever it were your duty to apprehend him?"

"Do? Why, yer blessed innocent, yer don't think I'd shirk a fair clean cop? Same time, I don't say as 'ow I wouldn't 'andle 'im tender like, for sake o' wot 'e wos. Likewise 'cos 'e'd be a stiff customer to tackle. Likewise 'cos—"

He had broken off, and was peering fixedly upwards at an angle of 85° across the moonlit street. "Ullo!" he said in a hoarse whisper.

Striking an average between the direction of his eyes—for Judlip, when on the job, has a soul-stirring squint—I perceived someone in the act of emerging from a chimney-pot.

Judlip's voice clove the silence. "Wot are yer doin' hup there?"

The person addressed came to the edge of the parapet. I saw then that he had a hoary white beard, a red ulster with the hood up, and what looked like a sack over his shoulder. He said something or other in a voice like a concertina that has been left in the rain.

"I dessay," answered my friend. "Just you come down, an' we'll see about that."

The old man nodded and smiled. Then—as I hope to be saved—he came floating gently down through the moonlight, with the sack over his shoulder and a young fir-tree

"I still say this is asinine, just to give her a rubber bone"

CPL. CHARLES CARTWRIGHT

(Reprinted from Collier's by permission.)

clasped to his chest. He alighted in a friendly manner on the curb beside us.

Judlip was the first to recover himself. Out went his right arm, and the airman was slung round by the scruff of the neck, spilling his sack in the road. I made a bee-line for his shoulder-blades. Burglar or no burglar, he was the best airman out, and I was muchly desirous to know the precise nature of the apparatus under his ulster. A back-hander from Judlip's left caused me to hop quickly aside. The prisoner was squealing and whimpering. He didn't like the feel of Judlip's knuckles at his cervical vertebrae.

"Wot was yer doin' hup there?" asked Judlip, rightening the grip.

"I'm S-Santa Claus, Sir. P-please, Sir, let me g-go."

"Hold him," I shouted. "He's a German."

"It's my dooty ter caution yer that wotever yer say now may be used in hevidence against yer, yer old sinner. Pick up that there sack, an' come along o' me."

The captive snivelled something about peace on earth, good will toward men.

"Yuss," said Judlip. "That's in the Noo Testament, ain't it? The Noo Testament contains some uncommon nice readin' for old gents an' young ladies. But it ain't included in the librery o' the Force. We confine ourselves to the Old Testament—O.T., 'ot. An' 'ot you'll get it. Hup with that sack, an' quick march!"

I have seen worse attempts at a neck-wrench, but it was just not slippery enough for Judlip. And the kick that Judlip then let fly was a thing of beauty and joy forever.

"Frog's-march him!" I shrieked, dancing. "For the love of heaven, frog's-march him!"

Trotting by Judlip's side to the Station, I reckoned it out that if Slushby had not been at the Club I should not have been here to see. Which shows that even Slushbys are put into the world for a purpose.

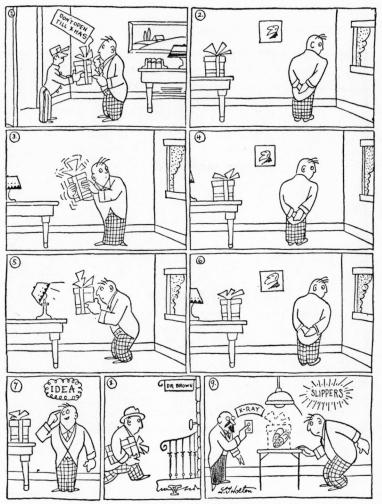

Don't Open Till Christmas!

MISTER BREGER

"Waaaaaa ... ! I want DADDY to see Santa Claus, too!"

Mr. Payson's
Satirical Christmas

GEORGE ADE

M R. SIDNEY PAYSON WAS FULL OF THE BITTERNESS OF
Christmas-tide. Mr. Payson was the kind of man who
loved to tell invalids that they were not looking as well
as usual, and who frightened young husbands by predicting
that they would regret having married. He seldom put the
seal of approval on any human undertaking. It was a matter
of pride with him that he never failed to find the sinister

motive for the act which other people applauded. Some of his pious friends used to say that Satan had got the upper hand with him, but there were others who indicated that it might be Bile.

Think of the seething wrath and the sense of humiliation with which Mr. Payson set about his Christmas shopping! In the first place, to go shopping for Christmas-presents was the most conventional thing anyone could do, and Mr. Payson hated conventionalities. For another thing, the giving of Christmas-presents carried with it some testimony of affection, and Mr. Payson regarded any display of affection as one of the crude symptoms of barbarous taste.

If he could have assembled his relatives at a Christmas-gathering and opened a few old family wounds, reminding his brother and his two sisters of some of their youthful follies, thus shaming them before the children, Mr. Sidney Payson might have managed to make out a rather merry Christmas. Instead of that, he was condemned to go out and purchase gifts and be as cheaply idiotic as the other wretched mortals with whom he was being carried along. No wonder that he chafed and rebelled and vainly wished that he could hang crepe on every Christmas tree in the universe.

Mr. Sidney Payson hated his task and was puzzled by it. After wandering through two stores and looking in at twenty windows he had been unable to make one selection. It seemed to him that all the articles offered for sale were singularly and uniformly inappropriate. The custom of giving was a farce in itself, and the store-keepers had done what they could to make it a sickening travesty.

"I'll go ahead and buy a lot of things at haphazard," he said to himself. "I don't care a hang whether they are appropriate or not."

At that moment he had an inspiration. It was an inspiration which could have come to no one except Mr. Sidney Payson. It promised a speedy end to shopping hardships. It guaranteed him a Christmas to his own liking.

He was bound by family custom to buy Christmas presents for his relatives. He had promised his sister that he would remember everyone on the list. But he was under no obligation to give presents that would be welcome. Why not give to each of his relatives some present which would be entirely useless, inappropriate, and superfluous? It would serve them right for involving him in the childish performances of the Christmas-season. It would be a burlesque on the whole nonsensicality of Christmas-giving. It would irritate and puzzle his relatives and probably deepen their hatred of him. At any rate, it would be a satire on a silly tradition and, thank goodness, it wouldn't be conventional.

Mr. Sidney Payson went into the first department-store and found himself at the book-counter.

"Have you any work which would be suitable for an elderly gentleman of studious habits and deep religious convictions?" he asked.

"We have here the works of Flavius Josephus in two volumes," replied the young woman.

"All right; I'll take them," he said. "I want them for my nephew Fred. He likes Indian stories."

The salesgirl looked at him wonderingly.

"Now, then, I want a love-story," said Mr. Payson. "I have a maiden sister who is president of a Ruskin club and writes essays about Buddhism. I want to give her a book that tells about a girl named Mabel who is loved by Sir Hextor Something-or-Other. Give me a book that is full of hugs and kisses and heaving bosoms and all that sort of rot. Get just as far away from Ibscn and Howells and Henry James as you can possibly get."

"Here is a book that all the girls in the store say is very good," replied the young woman. "It is called 'Virgie's Betrothal; or, the Stranger at Birchwood Manor.' It's by Imogene Sybil Beauclerc."

"If it's what it sounds to be, it's just what I want," said Payson, showing his teeth at the young woman with a devilish glee. "You say the girls here in the store like it?"

"Yes; Miss Simmons, in the handkerchief-box department, says it's just grand."

"Ha! All right! I'll take it."

He felt his happiness rising as he went out of the store. The joy shone in his face as he stood at the skate-counter.

"I have a brother who is forty-six years old and rather fat," he said to the salesman. "I don't suppose he's been on the ice in twenty-five years. He wears a number 9 shoe. Give me pair of skates for him."

A few minutes later he stood at the silk-counter.

"What are those things?" he asked, pointing to some gaily colored silks folded in boxes.

"Those are scarfs."

"Well, if you've got one that has all the colors of the rainbow in it, I'll take it. I want one with lots of yellow and red and green in it. I want something that you can hear across the street. You see, I have a sister who prides herself on her quiet taste. Her costumes are marked by what you call 'unobtrusive elegance.' I think she'd rather die than wear one of those things, so I want the biggest and noisiest one in the whole lot."

The girl didn't know what to make of Mr. Payson's strange remarks, but she was too busy to be kept wondering.

Mr. Payson's sister's husband is the president of a church temperance society, so Mr. Payson bought him a buckhorn corkscrew.

There was one more present to buy.

"Let me see," said Mr. Payson. "What is there that could be of no earthly use to a girl six years old?"

Even as he spoke his eyes fell on a sign: "Bargain sale of neckwear."

"I don't believe she would care for cravats," he said. "I think I'll buy some for her."

He saw a box of large cravats marked "25 cents each."

"Why are those so cheap?" he asked.

"Well, to tell the truth, they're out of style."

"That's good. I want eight of them—oh, any eight will

do. I want them for a small niece of mine—a little girl about six years old."

Without indicating the least surprise, the salesman wrapped up the cravats.

Letters received by Mr. Sidney Payson in acknowledgment of his Christmas-presents:

I

"Dear Brother:

"Pardon me for not having acknowledged the receipt of your Christmas-present. The fact is that since the skates came I have been devoting so much of my time to the re-acquiring of one of my early accomplishments that I have not had much time for writing. I wish I could express to you the delight I felt when I opened the box and saw that you had sent me a pair of skates. It was just as if you had said to me: 'Will, my boy, some people may think that you are getting on in years, but I know that you're not.' I suddenly remembered that the presents which I have been receiving for several Christmases were intended for an old man. I have received easy-chairs, slippers, mufflers, smoking-jackets, and the like. When I received the pair of skates from you I felt that twenty years had been lifted off my shoulders. How in the world did you ever happen to think of them? Did you really believe that my skating-days were not over? Well, they're *not!* I went to the pond in the park on Christmas-day and worked at it for two hours and I had a lot of fun. My ankles were rather weak and I fell down twice, fortunately without any serious damage to myself or the ice, but I managed to go through the motions, and before I left I skated with a smashing pretty girl. Well, Sid, I have you to thank. I never would have ventured on skates again if it had not been for you. I was a little stiff yesterday, but this morning I went out again and had a dandy time. I owe the renewal of my youth to you. Thank you many times, and believe me to be, as ever, your affectionate brother,

William."

II

"*Dear Brother:*

"The secret is out! I suspected it all the time! It is needless for you to offer denial. Sometimes when you have acted the cynic I have almost believed that you were sincere, but each time I have been relieved to observe in you something which told me that underneath your assumed indifference there was a genial current of the romantic sentiment of the youth and the lover. How can I be in doubt after receiving a little book—a love-story?

"I knew, Sidney dear, that you would remember me at Christmas. You have always been the soul of thoughtfulness, especially to those of us who understood you. I must confess, however, that I expected you to do the deadly conventional thing and send me something heavy and serious. I knew it would be a book. All my friends send me books. That comes of being president of a literary club. But you are the only one, Sidney, who had the rare and kindly judgment to appeal to the woman and not the club president. Because I am interested in a serious literary movement it need not follow that I want my whole life to be overshadowed by the giants of the kingdom of letters. Although

BRINGING IN THE BORE'S HEAD

I would not dare confess it to Mrs. Peabody or Mrs. Hutchens, there are times when I like to spend an afternoon with an old-fashioned love-story.

"You are a bachelor, Sidney, and as for me, I have long since ceased to blush at the casual mention of 'old maid.' It was not for us to know the bitter-sweet experience of courtship and marriage, and you will remember that we have sometimes pitied the headlong infatuation of sweethearts and have felt rather superior in our freedom. And yet, Sidney, if we chose to be perfectly candid with each other, I dare say that both of us would confess to having known something about that which men call *love*. We might confess that we had felt its subtle influence, at times and places, and with a stirring uneasiness, as one detects a draught. We might go so far as to admit that sometimes we pause in our lonely lives and wonder what might have been and whether it would not have been better, after all. I am afraid that I am writing like a sentimental school-girl, but you must know that I have been reading your charming little book, and it has come to me as a message from you. Is it not really a confession, Sidney?

"You have made me very happy, dear brother. I feel more closely drawn to you than at any time since we were all together at Christmas, at the old home. Come and see me. Your loving sister,

Gertrude."

III

"*Dear Brother:*

"Greetings to you from the happiest household in town, thanks to a generous Santa Claus in the guise of Uncle Sidney. I must begin by thanking you on my own account. How in the world did you ever learn that Roman colors have come in again? I had always heard that men did not follow the styles and could not be trusted to select anything for a woman, but it is a libel, for the scarf which you sent me is quite the most *beautiful* thing I have received this Christmas. I have it draped over the large picture in the parlor, and it is the envy of everyone who has been in to-day. A *thousand, thousand* thanks, dear Sidney. It was perfectly sweet of you to remember me, and I call it nothing less than a stroke of genius to think of anything so appropriate and yet so much out of the ordinary.

"John asks me to thank you—but I must tell you the story. One evening last week we had a little chafing-dish party after prayer-meeting, and I asked John to open a bottle of olives for me. Well, he broke the small blade of his knife trying to get the cork out. He said: 'If I live to get downtown again, I'm going to buy a corkscrew.' Fortunately he had neglected to buy one, and so your gift seemed to come straight from Providence. John is very much pleased. Already he has found use for it, as it happened that he wanted to open a bottle of household ammonia the very first thing this morning.

"As for Fred's lovely books, thank goodness you didn't send him any more story-books. John and I have been trying to induce him to take up a more serious line of reading. The Josephus ought to help him in the study of his Sunday-school lessons. We were pleased to observe that he read it for about an hour this morning.

"When you were out here last fall did Genevieve tell you that she was collecting silk for a doll quilt? She insists that she did not, but she must have done so, for how could you have guessed that she wants pieces of silk above anything else in the world? The perfectly lovely cravats which you sent will more than complete the quilt, and I think that mamma will get some of the extra pieces for herself. Fred and Genevieve send love and kisses. John insists that you come out to dinner some Sunday very soon—next Sunday if you can. After we received your presents we were quite ashamed of the box we had sent over to your hotel, but we will try to make up the difference in heart-felt gratitude. Don't forget—any Sunday. Your loving sister,

Katherine."

It would be useless to tell what Mr. Sidney Payson thought of himself after he received these letters.

IT ISN'T SO MUCH THE PRESENT ITSELF AS IT IS THE THOUGHT YOU PUT INTO IT

(Reproduced by permission.
Copyright 1931 by the New York Tribune, Inc.)

Dancing Dan's Christmas

DAMON RUNYON

Now ONE TIME IT COMES ON CHRISTMAS, AND IN FACT IT
is the evening before Christmas, and I am in Good
Time Charley Bernstein's little speakeasy in West Forty-
seventh Street, wishing Charley a Merry Christmas and
having a few hot Tom and Jerrys with him.

This hot Tom and Jerry is an old time drink that is once
used by one and all in this country to celebrate Christmas

with, and in fact it is once so popular that many people think Christmas is invented only to furnish an excuse for hot Tom and Jerry, although of course this is by no means true.

But anybody will tell you that there is nothing that brings out the true holiday spirit like hot Tom and Jerry, and I hear that since Tom and Jerry goes out of style in the United States, the holiday spirit is never quite the same.

Well, as Good Time Charley and I are expressing our holiday sentiments to each other over our hot Tom and Jerry, and I am trying to think up the poem about the night before Christmas and all through the house, which I know will interest Charley no little, all of a sudden there is a big knock at the front door, and when Charley opens the door, who comes in carrying a large package under one arm but a guy by the name of Dancing Dan.

This Dancing Dan is a good-looking young guy, who always seems well-dressed, and he is called by the name of Dancing Dan because he is a great hand for dancing around and about with dolls in night clubs, and other spots where there is any dancing. In fact, Dan never seems to be doing anything else, although I hear rumors that when he is not dancing he is carrying on in a most illegal manner at one thing and another. But of course you can always hear rumors in this town about anybody, and personally I am rather fond of Dancing Dan as he always seems to be getting a great belt out of life.

Anybody in town will tell you that Dancing Dan is a guy with no Barnaby whatever in him, and in fact he has about as much gizzard as anybody around, although I wish to say I always question his judgment in dancing so much with Miss Muriel O'Neill, who works in the Half Moon night club. And the reason I question his judgment in this respect is because everybody knows that Miss Muriel O'Neill is a doll who is very well thought of by Heine Schmitz, and Heine Schmitz is not such a guy as will take kindly to anybody dancing more than once and a half with a doll that he thinks well of.

Well, anyway, as Dancing Dan comes in, he weighs up the joint in one quick peek, and then he tosses the package he is carrying into a corner where it goes plunk, as if there is something very heavy in it, and then he steps up to the bar alongside of Charley and me and wishes to know what we are drinking.

Naturally we start boosting hot Tom and Jerry to Dancing Dan, and he says he will take a crack at it with us, and after one crack, Dancing Dan says he will have another crack, and Merry Christmas to us with it, and the first thing anybody knows it is a couple of hours later and we are still having cracks at the hot Tom and Jerry with Dancing Dan, and Dan says he never drinks anything so soothing in his life. In fact, Dancing Dan says he will recommend Tom and Jerry to everybody he knows, only he does not know anybody good enough for Tom and Jerry, except maybe Miss Muriel O'Neill, and she does not drink anything with drugstore rye in it.

Well, several times while we are drinking this Tom and Jerry, customers come to the door of Good Time Charley's little speakeasy and knock, but by now Charley is commencing to be afraid they will wish Tom and Jerry, too, and he does not feel we will have enough for ourselves, so he hangs out a sign which says "Closed on Account of Christmas," and the only one he will let in is a guy by the name of Ooky, who is nothing but an old rum-dum, and who is going around all week dressed like Santa Claus and carrying a sign advertising Moe Lewinsky's clothing joint around in Sixth Avenue.

This Ooky is still wearing his Santa Claus outfit when Charley lets him in, and the reason Charley permits such a character as Ooky in his joint is because Ooky does the porter work for Charley when he is not Santa Claus for Moe Lewinsky, such as sweeping out, and washing the glasses, and one thing and another.

Well, it is about nine-thirty when Ooky comes in, and his puppies are aching, and he is all petered out generally from walking up and down and here and there with his sign, for any time a guy is Santa Claus for Moe Lewinsky he must earn his dough. In fact, Ooky is so fatigued, and his puppies hurt him so much that Dancing Dan and Good Time Charley and I all feel very sorry for him, and invite him to have a few mugs of hot Tom and Jerry with us, and wish him plenty of Merry Christmas.

But old Ooky is not accustomed to Tom and Jerry and after about the fifth mug he folds up in a chair, and goes right to sleep on us. He is wearing a pretty good Santa Claus make-up, what with a nice red suit trimmed with white cotton, and a wig, and false nose, and long white whiskers, and a big sack stuffed with excelsior on his back, and if I do not know Santa Claus is not apt to be such a guy as will snore loud enough to rattle the windows, I will think Ooky is Santa Claus sure enough.

Well, we forget Ooky and let him sleep, and go on with our hot Tom and Jerry, and in the meantime we try to think up a few songs appropriate to Christmas, and Dancing Dan finally renders My Dad's Dinner Pail in a nice baritone and very loud, while I do first rate with Will You Love Me in December As You Do in May?

About midnight Dancing Dan wishes to see how he looks as Santa Claus.

So Good Time Charley and I help Dancing Dan pull off Ooky's outfit and put it on Dan, and this is easy as Ooky only has this Santa Claus outfit on over his ordinary clothes, and he does not even wake up when we are undressing him of the Santa Claus uniform.

Well, I wish to say I see many a Santa Claus in my time, but I never see a better looking Santa Claus than Dancing Dan, especially after he gets the wig and white whiskers fixed just right, and we put a sofa pillow that Good Time Charley happens to have around the joint for the cat to sleep on down his pants to give Dancing Dan a nice fat stomach such as Santa Claus is bound to have.

"Well," Charley finally says, "it is a great pity we do not know where there are some stockings hung up somewhere, because then," he says, "you can go around and stuff things in these stockings, as I always hear this is the main idea of a Santa Claus. But," Charley says, "I do not

suppose anybody in this section has any stockings hung
up, or if they have," he says, "the chances are they are so
full of holes they will not hold anything. Anyway," Charley
says, "even if there are any stockings hung up we do not
have anything to stuff in them, although personally," he
says, "I will gladly donate a few pints of Scotch."

Well, I am pointing out that we have no reindeer and
that a Santa Claus is bound to look like a terrible sap if
he goes around without any reindeer, but Charley's remarks seem to give Dancing Dan an idea, for all of a sudden he speaks as follows:

"Why," Dancing Dan says, "I know where a stocking
is hung up. It is hung up at Miss Muriel O'Neill's flat over
here in West Forty-ninth Street. This stocking is hung up
by nobody but a party by the name of Gammer O'Neill,
who is Miss Muriel O'Neill's grandmamma," Dancing Dan
says. "Gammer O'Neill is going on ninety-odd," he says,
"and Miss Muriel O'Neill tells me she cannot hold out
much longer, what with one thing and another, including
being a little childish in spots.

"Now," Dancing Dan says, "I remember Miss Muriel
O'Neill is telling me just the other night how Gammer
O'Neill hangs up her stocking on Christmas Eve all her
life, and," he says, "I judge from what Miss Muriel O'Neill
says that the old doll always believes Santa Claus will come
along some Christmas and fill the stocking full of beautiful gifts. But," Dancing Dan says, "Miss Muriel O'Neill
tells me Santa Claus never does this, although Miss Muriel
O'Neill personally always takes a few gifts home and pops

"I'll be glad when th' holidays is over. It raises heck
with my figure"

(Reprinted from Collier's by permission.)

them into the stocking to make Gammer O'Neill feel better.

"But, of course," Dancing Dan says, "these gifts are nothing much because Miss Muriel O'Neill is very poor, and proud, and also good, and will not take a dime off of anybody and I can lick the guy who says she will.

"Now," Dancing Dan goes on, "it seems that while Gammer O'Neill is very happy to get whatever she finds in her stocking on Christmas morning, she does not understand why Santa Claus is not more liberal, and," he says, "Miss Muriel O'Neill is saying to me that she only wishes she can give Gammer O'Neill one real big Christmas before the old doll puts her checks back in the rack.

"So," Dancing Dan states, "here is a job for us. Miss Muriel O'Neill and her grandmamma live all alone in this flat over in West Forty-ninth Street, and," he says, "at such an hour as this Miss Muriel O'Neill is bound to be working, and the chances are Gammer O'Neill is sound asleep, and we will just hop over there and Santa Claus will fill up her stocking with beautiful gifts."

Well, I say, I do not see where we are going to get any beautiful gifts at this time of night, what with all the stores being closed, unless we dash into an all-night drug store and buy a few bottles of perfume and a bum toilet set as guys always do when they forget about their everloving wives until after store hours on Christmas Eve, but Dancing Dan says never mind about this, but let us have a few more Tom and Jerrys first.

So we have a few more Tom and Jerrys, and then Dancing Dan picks up the package he heaves into the corner, and dumps most of the excelsior out of Ooky's Santa Claus sack, and puts the bundle in, and Good Time Charley turns out all the lights, but one, and leaves a bottle of Scotch on the table in front of Ooky for a Christmas gift, and away we go.

Personally, I regret very much leaving the hot Tom and Jerry, but then I am also very enthusiastic about going along to help Dancing Dan play Santa Claus, while Good Time Charley is practically overjoyed, as it is the first time in his life Charley is ever mixed up in so much holiday spirit.

As we go up Broadway, headed for Forty-ninth Street, Charley and I see many citizens we know and give them a large hello, and wish them Merry Christmas, and some of these citizens shake hands with Santa Claus, not knowing he is nobody but Dancing Dan, although later I understand there is some gossip among these citizens because they claim a Santa Claus with such a breath on him as our Santa Claus has is a little out of line.

And once we are somewhat embarrassed when a lot of little kids going home with their parents from a late Christmas party somewhere gather about Santa Claus with shouts of childish glee, and some of them wish to climb up Santa Claus' legs. Naturally, Santa Claus gets a little peevish, and calls them a few names, and one of the parents comes up and wishes to know what is the idea of Santa Claus using such language, and Santa Claus takes a punch at the parent, all of which is no doubt astonishing to the little kids who have an idea of Santa Claus as a very kindly old guy.

Well, finally we arrive in front of the place where Dancing Dan says Miss Muriel O'Neill and her grandmamma live, and it is nothing but a tenement house not far back of Madison Square Garden, and furthermore it is a walk-up, and at this time there are no lights burning in the joint except a gas jet in the main hall, and by the light of this jet we look at the names on the letter boxes, such as you always find in the hall of these joints, and we see that Miss Muriel O'Neill and her grandmamma live on the fifth floor.

This is the top floor, and personally I do not like the idea of walking up five flights of stairs, and I am willing to let Dancing Dan and Good Time Charley go, but Dancing Dan insists we must all go, and finally I agree with him because Charley is commencing to argue that the right way for us to do is to get on the roof and let Santa Claus go down a chimney, and is making so much noise I am afraid he will wake somebody up.

So up the stairs we climb and finally we come to a door on the top floor that has a little card in a slot that says O'Neill, so we know we reach our destination. Dancing Dan first tries the knob, and right away the door opens, and we are in a little two- or three-room flat, with not much furniture in it, and what furniture there is, is very poor. One single gas jet is burning near a bed in a room just off the one the door opens into, and by this light we

"You're missing half th' fun, Slug, not picking out th' presents yourself"

(Reprinted from Collier's by permission.)

see a very old doll is sleeping on the bed, so we judge this is nobody but Gammer O'Neill.

On her face is a large smile, as if she is dreaming of something very pleasant. On a chair at the head of the bed is hung a long black stocking, and it seems to be such a stocking as is often patched and mended, so I can see that what Miss Muriel O'Neill tells Dancing Dan about her grandmamma hanging up her stocking is really true, although up to this time I have my doubts.

Finally Dancing Dan unslings the sack on his back, and takes out his package, and unties this package, and all of a sudden out pops a raft of big diamond bracelets, and diamond rings, and diamond brooches, and diamond necklaces, and I do not know what else in the way of diamonds, and Dancing Dan and I begin stuffing these diamonds into the stocking and Good Time Charley pitches in and helps us.

There are enough diamonds to fill the stocking to the muzzle, and it is no small stocking, at that, and I judge that Gammer O'Neill has a pretty fair set of bunting sticks when she is young. In fact, there are so many diamonds that we have enough left over to make a nice little pile on the chair after we fill the stocking plumb up, leaving a nice diamond-studded vanity case sticking out the top where we figure it will hit Gammer O'Neill's eye when she wakes up.

And it is not until I get out in the fresh air again that all of a sudden I remember seeing large headlines in the afternoon papers about a five-hundred-G's stickup in the afternoon of one of the biggest diamond merchants in Maiden Lane while he is sitting in his office, and I also recall once hearing rumors that Dancing Dan is one of the best lone-hand git-'em-up guys in the world.

Naturally, I commence to wonder if I am in the proper company when I am with Dancing Dan, even if he is Santa Claus. So I leave him on the next corner arguing with Good Time Charley about whether they ought to go and find some more presents somewhere, and look for other stockings to stuff, and I hasten on home and go to bed.

The next day I find I have such a noggin that I do not care to stir around, and in fact I do not stir around much for a couple of weeks.

Then one night I drop around to Good Time Charley's little speakeasy, and ask Charley what is doing.

"Well," Charley says, "many things are doing, and personally," he says, "I'm greatly surprised I do not see you at Gammer O'Neill's wake. You know Gammer O'Neill leaves this wicked old world a couple of days after Christmas," Good Time Charley says, "and," he says, "Miss Muriel O'Neill states that Doc Moggs claims it is at least a day after she is entitled to go, but she is sustained," Charley says, "by great happiness in finding her stocking filled with beautiful gifts on Christmas morning.

"According to Miss Muriel O'Neill," Charley says, "Gammer O'Neill dies practically convinced that there is a Santa Claus, although of course," he says, "Miss Muriel O'Neill does not tell her the real owner of the gifts, an all-right guy by the name of Shapiro leaves the gifts with her after Miss Muriel O'Neill notifies him of the finding of same.

"It seems," Charley says, "this Shapiro is a tender-hearted guy, who is willing to help keep Gammer O'Neill with us a little longer when Doc Moggs says leaving the gifts with her will do it.

"So," Charley says, "everything is quite all right, as the coppers cannot figure anything except that maybe the rascal who takes the gifts from Shapiro gets conscience-stricken, and leaves them the first place he can, and Miss Muriel O'Neill receives a ten-G's reward for finding the gifts and returning them. And," Charley says, "I hear Dancing Dan is in San Francisco and is figuring on re-forming and becoming a dancing teacher, so he can marry Miss Muriel O'Neill, and of course," he says, "we all hope and trust she never learns any details of Dancing Dan's career."

Well, it is Christmas Eve a year later that I run into a guy by the name of Shotgun Sam, who is mobbed up with Heine Schmitz in Harlem, and who is a very, very obnoxious character indeed.

"Well, well, well," Shotgun says, "the last time I see you is another Christmas Eve like this, and you are coming out of Good Time Charley's joint, and," he says, "you certainly have your pots on."

"Well, Shotgun," I says, "I am sorry you get such a wrong impression of me, but the truth is," I say, "on the occasion you speak of, I am suffering from a dizzy feeling in my head."

"It is all right with me," Shotgun says. "I have a tip this guy Dancing Dan is in Good Time Charley's the night I see you, and Mockie Morgan, and Gunner Jack and me are casing the joint, because," he says, "Heine Schmitz is all sored up at Dan over some doll, although of course," Shotgun says, "it is all right now, as Heine has another doll.

"Anyway," he says, "we never get to see Dancing Dan. We watch the joint from six-thirty in the evening until daylight Christmas morning, and nobody goes in all night but old Ooky the Santa Claus guy in his Santa Claus makeup, and," Shotgun says, "nobody comes out except you and Good Time Charley and Ooky.

"Well," Shotgun says, "it is a great break for Dancing Dan he never goes in or comes out of Good Time Charley's, at that, because," he says, "we are waiting for him on the second-floor front of the building across the way with some nice little sawed-offs, and are under orders from Heine not to miss."

"Well, Shotgun," I say, "Merry Christmas."

"Well, all right," Shotgun says, "Merry Christmas."

"We should try to be broad-minded. After all, our own customs may seem just as strange to them"

(Reprinted from Collier's by permission.)

CUTIES ❖ By E. Simms Campbell

TELL
SANTA CLAUS
WHAT YOU
WANT FOR
CHRISTMAS

"You don't need to put girls THAT size on your lap!"

(Reprinted by permission.
Copyright 1950 by King Features Syndicate, Inc.)

89

Stephen Skarridge's Christmas

FRANK R. STOCKTON

'TWAS CHRISTMAS EVE. AN ADAMANTINE SKY HUNG DARK
and heavy over the white earth. The forests were ca-
nescent with frost, and the great trees bent as if they were
not able to sustain the weight of snow and ice with which
the young winter had loaded them.

In a by-path of the solemn woods there stood a cottage
that would not, perhaps, have been noticed in the decreas-

ing twilight, had it not been for a little wisp of smoke that
feebly curled from the chimney, apparently intending,
every minute, to draw up its attenuated tail, and disappear.
Within, around the hearth whereon the dying embers sent
up that feeble smoke, there gathered the family of Arthur
Tyrrell—himself, his wife, a boy, and a girl.

'Twas Christmas eve. A damp air rushed from the recesses of the forest and came, an unbidden guest, into the
cottage of the Tyrrells, and it sat on every chair, and lay
upon every bed, and held in its chilly embrace every member of the family. All sighed.

"Father," said the boy, "is there no more wood, that I
may replenish the fire?"

"No, my son," bitterly replied the father, his face hidden
in his hands; "I brought, at noon, the last stick from the
wood-pile."

The mother, at these words, wiped a silent tear from
her eyes, and drew her children yet nearer the smouldering
coals. The father rose and moodily stood by the window,
gazing out upon the night. A wind had now arisen, and
the dead branches strewed the path that he soon must
take to the neighboring town. But he cared not for the
danger; his fate and heart were alike hard.

"Mother!" said the little girl, "shall I hang up my stocking to-night? 'Tis Christmas eve."

A Damascus blade could not have cut the mother's heart
more keenly than this question.

"No, dear," she faltered. "You must wear your stockings
—there is no fire—and your feet, uncovered, will freeze."

The little girl sighed, and gazed sadly upon the blackening coals. But she raised her head again and said,

"But, mother dear, if I should sleep with my legs outside the clothes, old Santa Claus might slip in some little things between the stocking and my skin; could he not, dear mother?"

"Mother is weeping, sister," said the boy, "press her no further."

The father now drew around him his threadbare coat, put upon his head his well-brushed straw hat, and approached the door.

"Where are you going, this bitter night, dear father?" cried his little son.

"He goes," then said the weeping mother, "to the town. Disturb him not, my son, for he will buy a mackerel for our Christmas dinner."

"A mackerel!" cried both the children, and their eyes sparkled with joy. The boy sprang to his feet.

"You must not go alone, dear father," he cried. "I will accompany you."

And together they left the cottage.

The streets were crowded with merry faces and well wrapped-up forms. Snow and ice, it is true, lay thick upon the pavements and roofs, but what of that? Bright lights glistened from every window, bright fires warmed and softened the air within the houses, while bright hearts made rosy and happy the countenances of the merry crowd without. In some of the shops great turkeys hung in placid obesity from the bending beams, and enormous bowls of mince-meat sent up delightful fumes, which mingled harmoniously with the scents of the oranges, the apples, and the barrels of sugar and bags of spices. In others, the light from the chandeliers struck upon the polished surface of many a new wheelbarrow, sled, or hobby-horse, or lighted up the placid features of recumbent dolls and the demoniacal countenances of wildly jumping jacks. The crop of marbles and tops was almost more than could be garnered; boxes and barrels of soldiers stood on every side; tin horns hung from every prominence, and boxes of wonders filled the counters; while all the floor was packed with joyous children carrying their little purses. Beyond, there stood the candy-stores—those earthly paradises of the young, where golden gumdrops, rare cream chocolate, variegated mint-stick, and enrapturing mixtures spread their sweetened wealth over all available space.

To these and many other shops and stores and stalls and stands thronged the townspeople, rich and poor. Even the humblest had some money to spend upon this merry Christmas eve. A damsel of the lower orders might here be seen hurrying home with a cheap chicken; here another with a duck; and here the saving father of a family bending under the load of a turkey and a huge basket of good things. Everywhere were cheerful lights and warm hearthstones, bright and gay mansions, cosey and comfortable little tenements, happy hearts, rosy cheeks, and bright eyes. Nobody cared for the snow and ice, while they had so much that was warm and cheering. It was all the better for the holiday—what would Christmas be without snow?

Through these joyous crowds—down the hilarious streets, where the happy boys were shouting, and the merry girls were hurrying in and out of the shops—came a man who was neither joyous, hilarious, merry, nor happy. It was Stephen Skarridge, the landlord of many houses in that town. He wore an overcoat, which, though old, was warm and comfortable, and he had fur around his wrists and his neck. His hat was pushed down tight upon his little head, as though he would shut out all the sounds of merriment which filled the town. Wife and child he had none, and this season of joy to all the Christian world was an annoying and irritating season to his unsympathetic, selfish heart.

"Oh, ho!" he said to himself, as one after another of his tenants, loaded down with baskets and bundles, hurried by, each wishing him a merry Christmas; "oh, ho! there seems to be a great ease in the money market just now. Oh, ho, ho! They all seem as flush as millionnaires. There's nothing like the influence of holiday times to make one open his pockets—ha, ha! It's not yet the first of the month, 'tis true; but it matters not—I'll go and collect my rents to-night, while all this money is afloat—oh, ho! ha, ha!"

Now old Skarridge went from house to house, and threatened with expulsion all who did not pay their rents that night. Some resisted bravely, for the settlement day had not yet arrived, and these were served with notices to leave at the earliest legal moment; others paid up to their dues with many an angry protest; while some, poor souls had no money ready for this unforeseen demand, and Stephen Skarridge seized whatever he could find that would satisfy his claim. Thus many a poor, weeping family saw the turkey or the fat goose which was to have graced the Christmas table carried away by the relentless land-lord. The children shed tears to see their drums and toys depart, and many a little memento of affection, intended for a gift upon the morrow, became the property of the hard-hearted Stephen. 'Twas nearly nine o'clock when Skarridge finished his nefarious labor. He had converted his seizures into money, and was returning to his inhospi-table home with more joyous light in his eyes than had shone there for many a day, when he saw Arthur Tyrrell and his son enter the bright main street of the town.

"Oh, ho!" said Stephen; "has he, too, come to spend his Christmas money? He, the poor, miserable, penniless one! I'll follow him."

So behind the unhappy father and his son went the skulking Skarridge. Past the grocery store and the markets, with their rich treasures of eatables; past the toy-shops, where the boy's eyes sparkled with the delight which dis-appointment soon washed out with a tear; past the candy-shops, where the windows were so entrancing that the little fellow could scarcely look upon them—on, past all these, to a small shop at the bottom of the street, where a crowd of the very poorest people were making their lit-tle purchases, went the father and his son, followed by the evil-minded Skarridge. When the Tyrrells went into the shop, the old man concealed himself outside, behind a friendly pillar, lest any of these poor people should happen to be his tenants, and return him the damage he had just done to them. But he very plainly saw Arthur Tyrrell go up to the counter and ask for a mackerel. When one was brought, costing ten cents, he declined it, but eventually purchased a smaller one, the price of which was eight cents. The two cents which he received as change were expended for a modicum of lard, and father and son then left the store and wended their way homeward. The way was long, but the knowledge that they brought, that which would make the next day something more like Christmas than an ordinary day, made their steps lighter and the path less wearisome.

They reached the cottage and opened the door. There, by a rushlight on a table, sat the mother and the little girl, arranging greens wherewith to decorate their humble home. To the mute interrogation of the mother's eyes the father said, with something of the old fervor in his voice:

"Yes, my dear, I have brought it"; and he laid the mackerel on the table. The little girl sprang up to look at it, and the boy stepped back to shut the door; but before he could do so, it was pushed wide open, and Skarridge, who had followed them all the way, entered the cottage. The inmates gazed at him with astonishment; but they did not long remain in ignorance of the meaning of this untimely visit.

"Mr. Tyrrell," said Skarridge, taking out of his pocket a huge memorandum-book, and turning over the pages with a swift and practised hand, "I believe you owe me two months' rent. Let me see—yes, here it is—eighty-seven and a half cents—two months at forty-three and three-quarters cents per month. I should like to have it now, if you please," and he stood with his head on one side, his little eyes gleaming with a yellow maliciousness.

Arthur Tyrrell arose. His wife crept to his side, and the two children ran behind their parents.

"Sir," said Tyrrell, "I have no money—do your worst."

"No money!" cried the hard-hearted Stephen. "That story will not do for me. Everybody seems to have money to-night; and if they have none, it is because they have wilfully spent it. But if you really have none"—and here a ray of hope shot through the hearts of the Tyrrell family —"you must have something that will bring money, and that I shall seize upon. Ah, ha! I will take this!"

And he picked up the Christmas mackerel from the table where Arthur had laid it.

" 'Tis very little," said Skarridge, "but it will at least pay me my interest." Wrapping it in the brown paper which lay under it, he thrust it into his capacious pocket, and without another word went out into the night.

Arthur Tyrrell sank into a chair, and covered his face with his hands. His children, dumb with horror and dismay, clung to the rounds of his chair, while his wife, ever faithful in the day of sorrow as in that of joy, put her arm around his neck and whispered in his ear, "Cheer up, dear Arthur, all may yet be well; have courage! He did not take the lard!"

Swiftly homeward, through the forest, walked the triumphant Skarridge, and he reached his home an hour before midnight. He lived alone, in a handsome house (which he had seized for a debt), an old woman coming every day to prepare his meals and do the little housework that he required. Opening his door with his latch-key, he hurried upstairs, lighted a candle, and seating himself at a large table in a spacious room in the front of the house, he counted over the money he had collected that evening, entered the amount in one of the great folios which lay upon the table, and locked up the cash in a huge safe. Then he took from his pocket the mackerel of the Tyrrell family. He opened it, laid it flat upon the table before him, and divided it by imaginary lines into six parts.

"Here," said he to himself, "are breakfasts for six days —I would it were a week. I like to have things square and even. Had that man bought the ten-cent fish that I saw offered him, there would have been seven portions. Well, perhaps I can make it do, even now—let me see! A little off here—and the same off this—so———"

At this moment something very strange occurred. The mackerel, which had been lying, split open, upon its back, now closed itself, gave two or three long-drawn gasps, and then heaving a sigh of relief, it flapped its tail, rolled its eyes a little, and deliberately wriggling itself over to a pile of ledgers, sat up on its tail, and looked at Skarridge. This astounded individual pushed back his chair and gazed with all his eyes at the strange fish. But he was more astounded yet, when the fish spoke to him. "Would you mind," said the mackerel, making a very wry face, "getting me a glass of water? I feel all of a parch inside."

Skarridge mumbled out some sort of an assent, and hurried to a table near by, where stood a pitcher and a glass, and filling the latter, he brought it to the mackerel. "Will you hold it to my mouth?" said the fish. Stephen complying, the mackerel drank a good half of the water.

"There," it said, "that makes me feel better. I don't mind brine if I can take exercise. But to lie perfectly still in salt water makes one feel wretched. You don't know how hungry I am. Have you any worms convenient?"

"Worms!" cried Stephen, "why, what a question! No, I have no worms."

"Well," said the fish, somewhat petulantly, "you must have some sort of a yard or garden; go and dig me some."

"Dig them!" cried Stephen. "Do you know it's winter, and the ground's frozen—and the worms too, for that matter?"

"I don't care anything for all that," said the mackerel. "Go you and dig some up. Frozen or thawed, it is all one to me now; I could eat them anyway."

The manner of the fish was so imperative that Stephen Skarridge did not think of disobeying, but taking a crowbar and a spade from a pile of agricultural implements that lay in one corner of the room (and which had at various times been seized for debts), he lighted a lantern and went down into the little back garden. There he shovelled away the snow, and when he reached the ground he was obliged to use the crowbar vigorously before he could make any impression on the frozen earth. After a half-hour's hard labor, he managed, by most carefully searching through the earth thrown out of the hole he had made, to find five frozen worms. These he considered a sufficient meal for a fish which would scarcely make seven meals for himself, and so he threw down his implements and went into the house, with his lantern, his five frozen worms, and twice as many frozen fingers. When he reached the bottom of the stairs he was certain that he heard the murmur of voices from above. He was terrified. The voices came from the room where all his treasures lay! Could it be thieves?

Extinguishing his lantern and taking off his shoes, he softly crept up the stairs. He had not quite closed the door of the room when he left it, and he could now look through an opening which commanded a view of the whole apartment. And such a sight now met his wide-stretched eyes!

In his chair—his own arm-chair—by the table, there sat a dwarf, whose head, as large as a prize cabbage, was placed upon a body so small as not to be noticeable, and from which depended a pair of little legs appearing like the roots of the before-mentioned vegetable. On the table, busily engaged in dusting a day-book with a pen-wiper, was a fairy, no more than a foot high, and as pretty and graceful as a queen of the ballet viewed from the dress circle. The mackerel still leaned against the pile of ledgers;

and—oh horror!—upon a great iron box, in one corner, there sat a giant, whose head, had he stood up, would have reached the lofty ceiling!

A chill, colder than the frosty earth and air outside could cause, ran through the frame of Stephen Skarridge, as he crouched by the crack of the door and looked upon these dreadful visitors, while their conversation, of which he could hear distinctly every word, caused the freezing perspiration to trickle in icy globules down his back.

"He's gone to get me some worms," said the mackerel, "and we might as well settle it all before he comes back. For my part I'm very sure of what I have been saying."

"Oh, yes," said the dwarf; "there can be no doubt about it, at all. I believe it, every word."

"Of course it is so," said the fairy, standing upon the day-book, which was now well dusted; "everybody knows it is."

"It couldn't be otherwise," said the giant, in a voice like thunder among the pines; "we're all agreed upon that."

"They're mighty positive about it, whatever it is," thought the trembling Stephen, who continued to look with all his eyes and to listen with all his ears.

"Well," said the dwarf, leaning back in the chair and twisting his little legs around each other until they looked like a rope's end, "let us arrange matters. For my part, I would like to see all crooked things made straight, just as quickly as possible."

"So would I," said the fairy, sitting down on the day-book, and crossing her dainty satin-covered ankles, from which she stooped to brush a trifle of dust; "I want to see everything nice, and pretty, and just right."

"As for me," said the mackerel, "I'm somewhat divided —in my opinion, I mean—but whatever you all agree upon, will suit me, I'm sure."

"Then," said the giant, rising to his feet, and just escaping a violent contact of his head with the ceiling, "let us get to work, and while we are about it, we'll make a clean sweep of it."

To this the others all gave assent, and the giant, after moving the mackerel to one corner of the table, and requesting the fairy to stand beside the fish, spread all the ledgers, and day-books, and the cash, bill, and memorandum books upon the table, and opened each of them at the first page.

Then the dwarf climbed up on the table and took a pen, and the fairy did the same, and they both set to work, as hard as they could, to take an account of Stephen Skarridge's possessions. As soon as either of them had added up two pages the giant turned over the leaves, and he had to be very busy about it, so active was the dwarf, who had a splendid head for accounts, and who had balanced the same head so long upon his little legs that he had no manner of difficulty in balancing a few ledgers. The fairy, too, ran up and down the columns as if she were dancing a measure in which the only movements were "Forward one!" and "Backward one!" and she got over her business nearly as fast as the dwarf. As for the mackerel, he could not add up, but the fairy told him what figures she had to carry to the next column, and he remembered them for her, and thus helped her a great deal. In less than half an hour the giant turned over the last page of the last book, and the dwarf put down on a large sheet of foolscap the sum total of Stephen Skarridge's wealth.

The fairy read out the sum, and the woeful listener at the door was forced to admit to himself that they had got it exactly right.

"Now, then," said the giant, "here is the rent list. Let us make out the schedule." In twenty minutes the giant, the dwarf, and the fairy—the last reading out the names of Stephen's various tenants, the giant stating what amounts he deemed the due of each one, and the dwarf putting down the sums opposite their names—had made out the schedule, and the giant read it over in a voice that admitted of no inattention.

"Hurrah!" said the dwarf. "That's done, and I'm glad," and he stepped lightly from the table to the arm of the chair, and then down to the seat, and jumped to the floor, balancing his head in the most wonderful way, as he performed these agile feats.

"Yes," said the mackerel, "it's all right, though to be sure I'm somewhat divided——"

"Oh! we won't refer to that now," said the giant; "let by-gones be by-gones."

As for the fairy, she did not say a word, but she made a bounce to the top of the day-book which she had dusted, and which now lay closed near the edge of the table, and she danced such a charming little *fantaisie* that everybody gazed at her with delight. The giant stooped and opened his mouth as if he expected her to whirl herself into it when she was done; and the mackerel was actually moved to tears, and tried to wipe his eyes with his fin, but it was not long enough, and so the tears rolled down and hardened into a white crust on the green baize which covered the table. The dwarf was on the floor, and he stood motionless on his little toes, as if he had been a great top dead asleep. Even Stephen, though he was terribly agitated, thought the dance was the most beautiful thing he had ever seen. At length, with a whirl which made her look like a snow-ball on a pivot, she stopped stock-still, standing on one toe, as if she had fallen from the sky and had stuck upright on the day-book.

"Bravo! bravo!" cried the dwarf, and you could hear his little hands clapping beneath his head.

"Hurrah!" cried the giant, and he brought his great palms together with a clap that rattled the window-panes, like the report of a cannon.

"Very nice! very nice, indeed!" said the mackerel. "Though I'm rather di——"

"Oh, no, you're not!" cried the fairy, making a sudden joyful jump at him, and putting her little hand on his somewhat distorted and certainly very ugly mouth. "You're nothing of the kind, and now let's have him in here and make him sign. Do you think he will do it?" said she, turning to the giant. That mighty individual doubled up his great right fist like a trip-hammer, and he opened his great left hand, as hard and solid as an anvil, and he brought the two together with a sounding whang!

"Yes," said he, "I think he will."

"In that case," said the dwarf, "we might as well call him."

"I sent him after some worms," said the mackerel, "but he has not been all this time getting them. I should not wonder at all if he had been listening at the door all the while."

"We'll soon settle that," said the dwarf, walking rapidly across the room, his head rolling from side to side, but still preserving that admirable balance for which it was so justly noted. When he reached the door he pulled it wide open, and there stood poor Stephen Skarridge, trembling from head to foot, with the five frozen worms firmly grasped in his hands.

"Come in!" said the giant, and Stephen walked in slowly and fearfully, bowing as he came, to the several personages in the room.

"Are those my worms?" said the mackerel. "If so, put them in my mouth, one at a time. There! not so fast. They are frozen, sure enough; but do you know that I believe I like them this way the best. I never tasted frozen ones before."

By this time the dwarf had mounted the table, and opening the schedule, stood pointing to an agreement written at the bottom of it, while the fairy had a pen already dipped in the ink, which she held in her hand, as she stood on the other side of the schedule.

"Now, sir!" said the giant, "just take your seat in your chair, take that pen in your hand, and sign your name below that agreement. If you've been listening at the door all this time, as I believe you have, you have heard the contents of the schedule, and therefore need not read it over."

Stephen thought no more of disobeying than he did of challenging the giant to a battle, and he therefore seated himself in his chair, and taking the pen from the fairy, wrote his name at the bottom of the agreement, although he knew that by that act he was signing away half his wealth. When he had written his signature he laid down his pen and looked around to see if anything more was required of him; but just at that moment something seemed to give way in the back of his neck, his head fell forward so as to nearly strike the table, and he awoke!

There was no longer a schedule, a fairy, a dwarf, or a giant. In front of him was the mackerel, split open and lying on its back.

It was all a dream!

For an hour Stephen Skarridge sat at his table, his face buried in his hands. When, at last, his candle gave signs of spluttering out, he arose, and, with a subdued and quiet air, he went to bed.

The next morning was bright, cold, and cheering, and Stephen Skarridge arose very early, went down to the large front room where his treasures were kept, got out his checkbook, and for two hours was busily employed in writing. When the old woman who attended to his household affairs arrived at the usual hour, she was surprised at his orders to cook, for his breakfast, the whole of a mackerel which he handed her. When he had finished his meal, at which he ate at least one-half of the fish, he called her up into his room. He then addressed her as follows:

"Margaret, you have been my servant for seventeen years. During that time I have paid you fifty cents per week for your services. I am now convinced that the sum was insufficient; you should have had, at least, two dollars—considering you only had one meal in the house. As you would probably have spent the money as fast as I gave it to you, I shall pay you no interest upon what I have withheld, but here is a check for the unpaid balance—one thousand three hundred and twenty-six dollars. Invest it carefully, and you will find it quite a help to you." Handing the paper to the astounded woman, he took up a large wallet, stuffed with checks, and left the house.

He went down into the lower part of the town, with a countenance full of lively fervor and generous light. When he reached the quarter where his property lay, he spent an hour or two in converse with his tenants, and when he had spoken with the last one, his wallet was nearly empty, and he was followed by a wildly joyful crowd, who would have brought a chair and carried him in triumph through the town, had he not calmly waved them back.

When the concourse of grateful ones had left him, he repaired to the house of Philip Weaver, the butcher, and hired his pony and spring cart. Then he went to Ambrose Smith, the baker (at whose shop he had stopped on his way down-town), and inquired if his orders had been filled. Although it was Christmas morning, Ambrose and his seven assistants were all as busy as bees, but they had not yet been able to fill said orders. In an hour, however, Ambrose came himself to a candy store, where Stephen was treating a crowd of delighted children, and told him all was ready and the cart loaded. At this, Stephen hurried to the baker's shop, mounted the cart, took the reins, and drove rapidly in the direction of the cottage of Arthur Tyrrell. When he reached the place it was nearly one o'clock.

Driving cautiously, as he neared the house, he stopped at a little distance from it, and tied the horse to a tree. Then he stealthily approached a window and looked in.

Arthur Tyrrell sat upon a chair, in the middle of the room, his arms folded and his head bowed upon his breast. On a stool by his left side sat his wife, her tearful eyes raised to his sombre countenance. Before her father stood the little girl, leaning upon his knees and watching the varied expressions that flashed across his face. By his father's right side, his arm resting upon his parent's shoulder, stood the boy, a look of calm resignation far beyond his years lighting up his intelligent face.

'Twas a tableau never to be forgotten!

Able to gaze upon it but a few minutes, Stephen Skarridge pushed open the door and entered the room. His entrance was the signal of consternation. The wife and children fled to the farthest corner of the room, while Arthur Tyrrell arose and sternly confronted the intruder.

"Ha!" said he. "You have soon returned. You think that we can be yet further despoiled. Proceed, take all we have. There is yet this," and he pointed to the two cents' worth of lard, which still lay upon the table.

"No, no," faltered Stephen Skarridge, seizing the hand of Arthur Tyrrell and warmly pressing it. "Keep it! Keep it! 'Tis not for that I came, but to ask your pardon and to beg your acceptance of a Christmas gift. Pardon, for having increased the weight of your poverty, and a gift to celebrate the advent of a happier feeling between us."

Having said this, Stephen paused for a reply. Arthur Tyrrell mused for a moment; then he cast his eyes upon his wife and his children, and, in a low but firm voice, he said:

"I pardon and accept!"

"That's right!" cried Skarridge, his whole being animated by a novel delight; "come out to the cart, you and your son, and help me bring in the things, while Mrs. T. and the girl set the table as quickly as possible." The cart was now brought up before the door, and it was rapidly unloaded by willing hands. From under a half-dozen new blankets, which served to keep the other contents from contact with the frosty air, Stephen first handed out a fine linen table-cloth, and then a basket containing a dinner-set of queens-ware (third class—seventy-eight pieces with soup-tureen and pickle-dishes) and a half-dozen knives and forks (rubber-handled and warranted to stand hot water). When the cloth had been spread and the plates and dishes arranged, Arthur Tyrrell and his son, aided now by the wife and daughter, brought in the remaining contents of the cart and placed them on the table, while, with a bundle of kindling which he had brought, and the fallen limbs which lay all about the cottage, Skarridge made a rousing fire on the hearth.

When the cart was empty and the table fully spread, it presented indeed a noble sight. At one end a great turkey; at the other, a pair of geese; a duck upon one side and a pigeon-pie upon the other; cranberries, potatoes, white and sweet; onions, parsnips, celery, bread, butter, beets (pickled and buttered), pickled cucumbers, and walnuts, and several kinds of sauces, made up the first course; while upon a side-table stood mince-pies, apple-pies, pumpkin-pies, apples, nuts, almonds, raisins, and a huge pitcher of cider, for dessert.

It was impossible for the Tyrrell family to gaze unmoved upon this bounteously spread table, and after silently clasping each other for a moment, they sat down, with joyful, thankful hearts, to a meal far better than they had seen for years. At their earnest solicitation Mr. Skarridge joined them.

When the meal was over, and there was little left but empty dishes, they all arose, and Skarridge prepared to take his leave.

"But before I go," said he, "I would leave with you a further memento of my good feeling and friendship. You know my Hillsdale farm, in the next township?"

"Oh, yes!" cried Arthur Tyrrell; "is it possible that you will give me a position there?"

"I make you a present of the whole farm," said Skarridge.

"There are two hundred and forty-two acres, sixty of which are in timber; large mansion-house, two good barns, and cow and chicken houses; a well, covered in; an orchard of young fruit-trees, and a stream of water flowing through the place. The estate is well stocked with blooded cattle, horses, etc., and all necessary farming utensils. Possession immediate."

Without waiting for the dumfounded Tyrrell to speak, Skarridge turned quickly to his wife, and said: "Here, madam, is my Christmas-gift to you. In this package you will find shares of the New York Central and Hudson (sixes, of 'eighty-three), of the Fort Wayne (guaranteed), and of the St. Paul's (preferred); also bonds of the Delaware, Lackawanna, and Western (second mortgage), and of the Michigan Seven Per Cent. War Loan. In all these amount to nine thousand and eighty-two dollars; but to preclude the necessity of selling at a sacrifice, for immediate wants, I have taken the liberty of placing in the package one thousand dollars in greenbacks. And now, dear friends, adieu!"

But the grateful family could not allow this noble man to leave them thus. Arthur Tyrrell seized his hand and pressed it to his bosom, and then, as if overcome with emotion, Mrs. Tyrrell fell upon her benefactor's neck, while the children gratefully grasped the skirts of his coat. With one arm around the neck of the still young, once beautiful, and now fast improving Mrs. Tyrrell, Stephen Skarridge stood for a few minutes, haunted by memories of the past. Then he spoke:

"Once," said he, his voice trembling the while, "once—I, too—loved such a one. But it is all over now—and the grass waves over her grave. Farewell, farewell dear friends!" and dashing away a tear, he tore himself from the fervent family, and swiftly left the house.

Springing into the cart, he drove rapidly into the town— a happy man! . . .

Did you ever before read a story like this?

113

Mr. Kaplan
and the Magi

LEONARD Q. ROSS

WHEN MR. PARKHILL SAW THAT MISS MITNICK, MR. Bloom, and Mr. Hyman Kaplan were absent, and that a strange excitement pervaded the beginners' grade, he realized that it was indeed the last night before the holidays and that Christmas was only a few days off. Each Christmas the classes in the American Night Preparatory School for Adults gave presents to their respective teachers. Mr. Parkhill, a veteran of many sentimental Yuletides, had come to know the procedure. That night, before the class session, had begun, there must have been a hurried collection; a Gift Committee of three had been chosen; at this moment the Committee was probably in Mickey Goldstein's Arcade, bargaining feverishly, arguing about the appropriateness of a pair of pajamas or the color of a dozen linen handkerchiefs, debating whether Mr. Parkhill would prefer a pair of fleece-lined slippers to a set of mother-of-pearl cuff links.

"We shall concentrate on—er—spelling drill tonight," Mr. Parkhill announced.

The students smiled wisely, glanced at the three empty seats, exchanged knowing nods, and prepared for spelling drill. Miss Rochelle Goldberg giggled, then looked ashamed as Mrs. Rodriguez shot her glare of reproval.

Mr. Parkhill always chose a spelling drill for the night before the Christmas vacation: it kept all the students busy simultaneously; it dampened the excitement of the occasion; above all, it kept him from the necessity of resorting to elaborate pedagogical efforts in order to hide his own embarrassment.

Mr. Parkhill called off the first words. Pens and pencils scratched, smiles died away, eyes grew serious, preoccupied, as the beginners' grade assaulted the spelling of "Banana . . . Romance . . . Groaning." Mr. Parkhill sighed. The class seemed incomplete without its star student, Miss Mitnick, and barren without its most remarkable one, Mr. Hyman Kaplan. Mr. Kaplan's most recent linguistic tri-

(The Saturday Evening Post)

umph had been a fervent speech extolling the D'Oyly Carte Company's performance of an operetta by two English gentlemen referred to as "Goldberg and Solomon."

"Charming . . . Horses . . . Float," Mr. Parkhill called off.

Mr. Parkhill's mind was not really on "Charming . . . Horses . . . Float." He could not help thinking of the momentous event which would take place that night. After the recess the students would come in with flushed faces and shining eyes. The Committee would be with them, and one member of the Committee, carrying an elaborately bound Christmas package, would be surrounded by several of the largest students in the class, who would try to hide the parcel from Mr. Parkhill's eyes. The class would come to order with uncommon rapidity. Then, just as Mr. Parkhill resumed the lesson, one member of the Committee would rise, apologize nervously for interrupting, place the package on Mr. Parkhill's desk, utter a few half-swallowed words, and rush back to his or her seat. Mr. Parkhill would say a few halting phrases of gratitude and surprise, everyone would smile and fidget uneasily, and the lesson would drag on, somehow, to the final and distant bell.

"Accept . . . Except . . . Cucumber."

And as the students filed out after the final bell, they would cry "Merry Christmas, Happy New Year!" in joyous voices. The Committee would crowd around Mr. Parkhill with tremendous smiles to say that if the present wasn't *just right* in size or color (if it was something to wear) or in design (if it was something to use), Mr. Parkhill could exchange it. He didn't *have* to abide by the Committee's choice. He could exchange the present for *any*thing. They would have arranged all that carefully with Mr. Mickey Goldstein himself.

That was the ritual, fixed and unchanging, of the last night of school before Christmas.

"Nervous . . . Goose . . . Violets."

The hand on the clock crawled around to eight. Mr. Parkhill could not keep his eyes off the three seats, so eloquent in their vacancy, which Miss Mitnick, Mr. Bloom, and Mr. Kaplan ordinarily graced with their presences. He could almost see these three in the last throes of decision in Mickey Goldstein's Arcade, harassed by the competitive attractions of gloves, neckties, an electric clock, a cane, spats, a fountain pen. Mr. Parkhill grew cold at the thought. Three times already he had been presented with fountain pens, twice with pencils to match. Mr. Parkhill had, of course, exchanged them. Once he had chosen a woolen vest instead; once a pair of mittens and a watch chain. Also Mr. Parkhill hoped it wouldn't be a smoking jacket. He had never been able to understand how the Committee that year had decided upon a smoking jacket. Mr. Parkhill did not smoke. He had exchanged it for fur-lined gloves.

Just as Mr. Parkhill called off "Sardine . . . Exquisite . . . Palace" the recess bell rang. The heads of the students bobbed up as if propelled by a single spring.

There was a rush to the door, Mr. Sam Pinsky well in

the lead. Then, from the corridor, their voices rose. Mr. Parkhill began to print "Banana" on the blackboard, so that the students could correct their own papers after recess. He tried not to listen, but the voices in the corridor were like the chatter of a flock of sparrows.

"Hello, Mitnick!"

"Bloom, Bloom, vat is it?"

"So vat did you gat, Keplen? Tell!"

Mr. Parkhill could hear Miss Mitnick's shy "We bought—" interrupted by Mr. Kaplan's stern cry, "Mitnick! Don' say! Plizz, faller-students! Come *don* mit de voices! Titcher vill awreddy hearink, you hollerink so lod! Still! Order! Plizz!" There was no question about it: Mr. Kaplan was born to command.

"Did you bought a fontain pan sat, guarantee for de whole life, like *I* said?" one voice came through the door. A fountain pen set, guaranteed. That was Mrs. Moskowitz. Poor Mrs. Moskowitz, she showed so little imagination, even in her homework. "Moskovitz! Mein Gott!" the stentorian whisper of Mr. Kaplan soared through the air. "Vy you don' open op de door Titcher should *positivel* hear? Ha! Let's goink to odder and fromm de hall!"

The voices of the beginners' grade died away as they moved to the "odder and" of the corridor, like the chorus of Aïda vanishing into Egyptian wings.

Mr. Parkhill printed "Charming" and "Horses" on the board. For a moment he thought he heard Mrs. Moskowitz's voice repeating stubbornly, "Did—you—bought—a —fontain—pan—sat—*guarantee?*"

"What will you take for the stockings?"

(Reprinted by permission of
the Proprietors of Punch.)

Mr. Parkhill began to say to himself, "Thank you, all of you. It's *just* what I wanted," again and again. One Christmas he hadn't said "It's just what I wanted" and poor Mrs. Oppenheimer, chairman of the Committee that year, had been hounded by the students' recriminations for a month.

It seemed an eternity before the recess bell rang again. The class came in *en masse*, and hastened to the seats from which they would view the impending spectacle. The air hummed with silence.

Mr. Parkhill was printing "Cucumber." He did not turn his face from the board as he said, "Er—please begin correcting your own spelling. I have printed most of the words on the board."

There was a low and heated whispering. "Stend op, Mitnick!" he heard Mr. Kaplan hiss. "You should stend op too!"

"The *whole* Committee," Mr. Bloom whispered. "Stand op!"

Apparently Miss Mitnick, a gazelle choked with embarrassment, did not have the fortitude to "stend op" with her colleagues.

"A fine raprezantitif *you'll* gonna make!" Mr. Kaplan hissed scornfully. "Isn't for *mine* sek I'm eskink, Mitnick. Plizz *stend op!*"

There was a confused, half-muted murmur, and the anguished voice of Miss Mitnick saying, "I *can't*." Mr. Parkhill printed "Violets" on the board. Then there was a tense silence. And then the voice of Mr. Kaplan rose, firmly, clearly, with a decision and dignity which left no doubt as to its purpose.

"Podden me, Mr. Pockheel!"

It had come.

"Er—yes?" Mr. Parkhill turned to face the class.

Messrs. Bloom and Kaplan were standing side by side in front of Miss Mitnick's chair, holding between them a large, long package, wrapped in cellophane and tied with huge red ribbons. A pair of small hands touched the bottom of the box, listlessly. The owner of the hands, seated in the front row, was hidden by the box.

"De hends is Mitnick," Mr. Kaplan said apologetically.

Mr. Parkhill gazed at the tableau. It was touching.

"Er—yes?" he said again feebly, as if he had forgotten his lines and was repeating his cue.

"Hau Kay!" Mr. Kaplan whispered to his confreres. The hands disappeared behind the package. Mr. Kaplan and Mr. Bloom strode to the platform with the box. Mr. Kaplan was beaming, his smile rapturous, exalted. They placed the package on Mr. Parkhill's desk, Mr. Bloom dropped back a few paces, and Mr. Kaplan said, "Mr. Pockheel! Is mine beeg honor, becawss I'm Chairman fromm de Buyink an' Deliverink to You a Prazent Committee, to givink to you dis fine peckitch."

Mr. Parkhill was about to stammer, "Oh, thank you," when Mr. Kaplan added hastily, "Also I'll sayink a few voids."

Mr. Kaplan took an envelope out of his pocket. He whispered loudly, "*Mitnick, you still got time to comm op*

mit de Committee," but Miss Mitnick only blushed furi-
ously and lowered her eyes. Mr. Kaplan sighed, straightened the envelope, smiled proudly at Mr. Parkhill, and
read.

"Dear Titcher—dat's de beginnink. Ve stendink on de
adge fromm a beeg holiday." He cleared his throat. "Ufcawss is all kinds holidays in U.S.A. Holidays for politic, for
religious, an' *plain* holidays. In Fabrary, ve got Judge Vash-
ington's boitday, a *fine* holiday. Also Abram Lincohen's. In
May ve got Memorable Day, for dad soldiers. In July
comms, netcheral, Fort July. Also ve have Labor Day,
Denksgivink, for de Peelgrims, an' for de feenish fromm de
Voild Var, Armistress Day."

Mr. Parkhill played with a piece of chalk nervously.

"But arond dis time year ve have a *difference* kind holiday, a spacial, movvellous time. Dat's called—Chrissmas."

Mr. Parkhill put the chalk down.

"All hover de voild," Mr. Kaplan mused, "is pipple cele-
braking dis vunderful time. Becawss of som pipple is Chrissmas like for *odder* pipple is Passover. Or Chanukah, batter.
De most fine, de most beauriful, de most *secret* holiday
fromm de whole bunch!"

(" 'Sacred,' Mr. Kaplan, 'sacred,' " Mr. Parkhill thought,
ever the pedagogue.)

"Ven ve valkink don de stritt an' is snow on de floor an'
all kinds tarrible cold!" Mr. Kaplan's hand leaped up dra-
matically, like a flame. "Ven ve see in de vindows trees
mit rad an' grin laktric lights boinink! Ven is de time for
tellink de fancy-tales about Sandy Claws commink fromm

Naut Pole on rain-enimals, an' climbink don de jiminies mit *stockings* for all de leetle kits! Ven ve hearink abot de beauriful toughts of de Tree Vise Guys who vere follerink a star fromm de dasert! Ven pipple saying, 'Oh, Mary Chrissmas! Oh, Heppy Noo Yiss! Oh, bast regotts!' Den ve *all* got a varm fillink in de heart for all humanity vich should be brodders!"

Mr. Feigenbaum nodded philosophically at this profound thought; Mr. Kaplan, pleased, nodded back.

"*You* got de fillink, Mr. Pockheel. *I* got de fillink, dat's no qvastion abot! Bloom, Pinsky, Caravello, Schneiderman, even Mitnick—" Mr. Kaplan was punishing Miss Mitnick tenfold for her perfidy—"got de fillink! An' vat is it?" There was a momentous pause. "De Chrissmas Spirits!"

(" 'Spirit,' Mr. Kaplan, 'spirit,' " the voice of Mr. Parkhill's conscience said.)

"Now I'll givink de prazent," Mr. Kaplan announced subtly. Mr. Bloom shifted his weight. "Becawss you a foistclass titcher, Mr. Pockheel, an' learn abot gremmer an' spallink an' de hoddest pots pernonciation—ve know is a planty hod job mit soch students—so ve fill you should havink a sample fromm our—fromm our—" Mr. Kaplan turned the envelope over hastily—"aha! Fromm our santimental!"

Mr. Parkhill stared at the long package.

"Fromm de cless, to our lovely Mr. Pockheel!"

Mr. Parkhill started. "Er—?" he asked involuntarily.

"Fromm de cless, to our lovely Mr. Pockheel!" Mr. Kaplan repeated with pride.

(" 'Beloved,' Mr. Kaplan, 'beloved.' ")

A hush had fallen over the room. Mr. Kaplan, his eyes bright with joy, waited for Parkhill to take up the ritual. Mr. Parkhill tried to say, "Thank you, Mr. Kaplan," but the phrase seemed meaningless, so big, so ungainly, that it could not get through his throat. Without a word Mr. Parkhill began to open the package. He slid the big red ribbons off. He broke the tissue paper inside. For some reason his vision was blurred and it took him a moment to identify the present. It was a smoking jacket. It was black and gold, and a dragon with a green tongue was embroidered on the pocket.

"Horyantal style," Mr. Kaplan whispered.

Mr. Parkhill nodded. The air trembled with the tension. Miss Mitnick looked as if she were ready to cry. Mr. Bloom peered intently over Mr. Kaplan's shoulder. Mrs. Moskowitz sat entranced, sighing with behemothian gasps. She looked as if she were at her daughter's wedding.

"Thank you," Mr. Parkhill stammered at last. "Thank you, all of you."

Mr. Bloom said, "Hold it op everyone should see."

Mr. Kaplan turned on Mr. Bloom with an icy look. "I'm de chairman!" he hissed.

"I—er—I can't tell you how much I appreciate your kindness," Mr. Parkhill said without lifting his eyes.

Mr. Kaplan smiled. "So now you'll plizz hold op de prazent. Plizz."

Mr. Parkhill took the smoking jacket out of the box and

held it up for all to see. There were gasps—"Oh!s" and "Ah!s" and Mr. Kaplan's ecstatic "My! Is beauriful!"

"Maybe ve made a mistake," Mr. Kaplan said hastily. "Maybe you don' smoke—dat's how *Mitnick* tought." The scorn dripped. "But I said, 'Ufcawss is Titcher smokink! Not in de cless, netcheral. At home! At least a pipe!'"

"No, no, you didn't make a mistake. It's—it's *just* what I wanted!"

The great smile on Mr. Kaplan's face became dazzling. "Hooray! Vear in de bast from helt!" he cried impetuously. "Mary Chrissmas! Heppy Noo Yiss! You should have a *hondert* more!"

This was the signal for a chorus of acclaim. "Mary Chrissmas!" "Wear in best of health!" "Happy New Year!" Miss Schneiderman burst into applause, followed by Mr. Scymzak and Mr. Weinstein. Miss Caravello, carried away by all the excitement, uttered some felicitations in Italian.

The ceremony was over. Mr. Parkhill began to put the smoking jacket back into the box with fumbling hands. Mr. Bloom marched back to his seat. But Mr. Kaplan stepped a little closer to the desk. The smile had congealed on Mr. Kaplan's face. It was poignant and profoundly earnest.

"Er—thank you, Mr. Kaplan," Mr. Parkhill said gently.

Mr. Kaplan shuffled his feet, looking at the floor. For the first time since Mr. Parkhill had known him, Mr. Kaplan seemed to be embarrassed. Then, just as he turned to rush back to his seat, Mr. Kaplan whispered, so softly that no ears but Mr. Parkhill's heard it, "Maybe de spitch I rad vas too *formmal*. But avery void I said—it came fromm *below mine heart!*"

Mr. Parkhill felt that, for all his unorthodox English, Mr. Kaplan had spoken with the tongues of the Magi.

"Oh, boy. Just what I needed! Aspirin!"   GARDNER REA

(Reprinted from Collier's by permission.)

The Worst Christmas Story

CHRISTOPHER MORLEY

WE HAD BEEN DOWN TO AN EAST SIDE SETTLEMENT house on Christmas afternoon. I had watched my friend Dove Dulcet, in moth-riddled scarlet and cotton wool trimmings, play Santa Claus for several hundred adoring urchins and their parents. He had done this for many years, but I had never before seen him insist upon the amiable eccentricity of returning uptown still wearing the regalia of the genial saint. But Dove is always unusual, and I thought—as did the others who saw him, in the subway and elsewhere—it was a rather kindly and innocent concession to the hilarity of the day.

When we had got back to his snug apartment he beamed at me through his snowy fringes of false whiskers, and began rummaging in the tall leather boots of his costume. From each one he drew a bottle of chianti.

"From a grateful parent on Mulberry Street," he said. "My favorite bootlegger lives down that way, and I've been playing Santa to his innumerable children for a number of years. The garb attributed—quite inaccurately, I expect—to Saint Nicholas of Bari, has its uses. Even the keenest revenue agent would hardly think of holding up poor old Santa."

He threw off his trappings, piled some logs on the fire, and we sat down for our annual celebration. Dove and I have got into the habit of spending Christmas together. We are both old bachelors, with no close family ties, and we greatly enjoy the occasion. It isn't wholly selfish, either, for we usually manage to spice our fun with a little unexpected charity in some of the less fortunate quarters of the town.

As my friend uncorked the wicker-bound bottles I noticed a great pile of Christmas mail on his table.

"Dove, you odd fish," I said. "Why don't you open your letters? I should have thought that part of the fun of Christmas is hurrying to look through the greetings from friends. Or do you leave them to the last, to give them greater savor?"

He glanced at the heap, with a curious expression on his face.

"The Christmas cards?" he said. "I postpone them as long as I possibly can. It's part of my penance."

"What on earth do you mean?"

He filled two glasses, passed one to me, and sat down beside the cheerful blaze.

"Here's luck, old man!" he said. "Merry Christmas."

I drank with him, but something evasive in his manner impelled me to repeat my question.

"What a ferret you are, Ben!" he said. "Yes, I put off looking at the Christmas cards as long as I dare. I suppose I'll have to tell you. It's one of the few skeletons in my anatomy of melancholy that you haven't exhumed. It's a queer kind of Christmas story."

He reached over to the table, took up a number of the envelopes, and studied their handwritings. He tore them open one after another, and read the enclosed cards.

"As I expected," he said. "Look here, it's no use your trying to make copy out of this yarn. No editor would look at it. It runs counter to all the good old Christmas tradition."

"My dear Dove," I said, "if you've got a Christmas story that's 'different,' you've got something that editors will pay double for."

"Judge for yourself," he said. From the cards in his lap

he chose four and gave them to me. "Begin by reading those."

Completely mystified I did so.

The first showed a bluebird perched on a spray of holly. The verse read:

> Our greeting is "Merry Christmas!"
> None better could we find,
> And tho' you are now out of sight,
> You're ever in our mind.

The second card said, below a snow scene of mid-Victorian characters alighting from a stagecoach at the hospitable door of a country mansion:

Should you or your folk ever call at our door
You'll be welcome, we promise you—nobody more;
We wish you the best of the Joy and Cheer
That can come with Christmas and last through the year!

The third, with a bright picture of the three stout old gentlemen in scarlet waistcoats, tippling before an open fire:

Jolly old Yule, Oh the jolly old Yule
Blesses rich man and poor man and wise man and fool—
Be merry, old friend, in this bright winter weather,
And you'll Yule and I'll Yule, we'll all Yule together!

The fourth—an extremely ornate vellum leaflet, gilded with Oriental designs and magi on camels—ran thus:

I pray the prayer the Easterners do;
May the Peace of Allah abide with you—
Through days of labor and nights of rest
May the love of Allah make you blest.

"Well," I said, "of course I wouldn't call them great poetry, but the sentiments are generous enough. Surely it's the spirit in which they're sent that counts. It doesn't seem like you to make fun—"

Dulcet leaned forward. "Make fun?" he said. "Heavens, I'm not making fun of them. The ghastly thing is, I wrote those myself."

There was nothing to say, so I held my peace.

"You didn't know, I trust, that at one time I was re-garded as the snappiest writer of greeting sentiments (so the trade calls them) in the business? That was long ago, but the sentiments themselves, and innumerable imitations of them, go merrily on. You see, out of the first ten cards that I picked up, four are my own composition. Can you imagine the horror of receiving, every Christmas, every New Year, every Easter, every birthday, every Halloween, every Thanksgiving, cards most of which were written by yourself? And when I think of the honest affection with which those cards were chosen for me by my unsuspecting friends, and contrast their loving simplicity with—"

He broke off, and refilled the glasses.

"I told you," he said, "that this was the worst Christmas story in the world! But I must try to tell it a little better, at any rate. Well, it has some of the traditional ingredients.

"You remember the winter of the Great Panic—1906,

wasn't it? I had a job in an office downtown, and was laid off. I applied everywhere for work—nothing doing. I had been writing a little on the side, verses and skits for the newspapers, but I couldn't make enough that way to live on. I had an attic in an old lodging house on Gay Street. (The Village was still genuine then, no hokum about it.) I used to reflect on the irony of that name, Gay Street, when I was walking about trying not to see the restaurants, they made me feel so hungry. I still get a queer feeling in the pit of my stomach when I pass by Gonfarone's—there was a fine thick savor of spaghetti and lentil soup that used to float out from the basement as I went along Eighth Street.

"There was a girl in it too, of course. You'll smile when I tell you who she was. Peggy Cassell, who does the magazine covers. Yes, she's prosperous enough now—so are we all. But those were the days!

"It's the old bachelors who are the real sentimentalists, hey? But by Jove, how I adored that girl! She was fresh from upstate somewhere, studying at the League, and doing small illustrating jobs to make ends approach. I was as green and tender as she. I was only twenty-five, you know. To go up to what Peggy called her studio—which was only a bleak bedroom which she shared with another girl—and smoke cigarettes and see her wearing a smock and watch her daub away at a thing she intended to be a 'portrait' of me, was my idea of high tide on the seacoast of Bohemia. Peggy would brew cocoa in a chafing dish and then the other girl would tactfully think of some errand, and we'd sit, timidly and uncomfortably, with our arms around each other, and talk about getting married some day, and prove by Cupid's grand old logarithms that two can live cheaper than one. I used to recite to her that ripping old song, 'My Peggy is a young thing, And I'm not very auld,' and it would knock us both cold.

"The worst of it was, poor Peggy was almost as hard up as I was. In fact, we were both so hard up that I'm amazed we didn't get married, which is what people usually do when they have absolutely no prospects. But with all her sweet sentiment Peggy had a streak of sound caution. And as a matter of fact, I think she was better off than I was, because she did get a small allowance from home. Anyway, I was nearly desperate, tearing my heart out over the thought of this brave little creature facing the world for the sake of her art, and so on. She complained of the cold, and I remember taking her my steamer rug off my own bed, telling her I was too warm. After I used to shingle myself over with newspapers when I went to bed. It was bitter on Gay Street that winter.

"But I said this was a Christmas Story. So it is. It began like this. About Halloween I had a little poem in *Life*— nothing of any account, but a great event to me, my first appearance in Big Time journalism. Well, one day I got a letter from a publisher in Chicago asking permission to reprint it on a card. He said also that my verses had just the right touch which was needed in such things, and that I could probably do some 'holiday greetings' for him. He would be glad to see some Christmas 'sentiments,' he said, and would pay one dollar each for any he could use.

"You can imagine that it didn't take me long to begin tearing off sentiments though I stipulated, as a last concession to my honor, that my name should not be used. There was no time to lose: it was now along in November, and these things—to be sold to the public for Christmas a year later—must be submitted as soon as possible so that they could be illustrated and ready for the salesmen to take on the road in January.

"Picture, then, the young author of genial greeting cards, sitting ironically in the chilliest attic on Gay Street—a dim and draughty little elbow of the city—and attempting to ignite his wits with praise of the glowing hearth and the brandied pudding. The room was heated only by a small gas stove, one burner of which had been scientifically sealed by the landlady; an apparatus, moreover, in which asphyxia was the partner of warmth. When that sickly sweetish gust became too overpotent, see the author throw up the window and retire to bed, meditating under a mountain of news-print further applause of wintry joy and fellowship. I remember one sentiment—very likely it is among the pile on the table here: it is a great favorite—which went:

> May blazing log and steaming bowl
> And wreaths of mistletoe and holly
> Remind you of a kindred soul
> Whose love for you is warm and jolly!

"My, how cold it was the night I wrote that."

Dove paused, prodded the logs to a brighter flame, and

leaned closer to the chimney as though feeling a reminiscent chill.

"Well, as Christmas itself drew nearer, I became more and more agitated. I had sent in dozens of these compositions; each batch was duly acknowledged, and highly praised. The publisher was pleased to say that I had a remarkable aptitude for 'greetings'; my Christmas line, particularly, he applauded as being full of the robust and hearty spirit of the old-fashioned Yule. My Easter touch, he felt, was a little thin and tepid by comparison. So I redoubled my metrical cheer. I piled the logs higher and higher upon my imaginary hearth; I bore in cups of steaming wassail; blizzards drummed at my baronial window panes; stagecoaches were halted by drifts axle-deep; but within the circle of my mid-Victorian halloo, all was mirth; beauty crowded beneath the pale mistletoe; candles threw a tawny shine; the goose was carved and the port wine sparkled. And all the while, if you please, it was December of the panic winter; no check had yet arrived from the delighted publisher; I had laid aside other projects to persue this golden phantom; I ate once a day, and sometimes kept warm by writing a mellow outburst of gladness in the steam-heated lobbies of hotels.

"I had said nothing to Peggy about this professional assumption of Christmas heartiness. For one thing, I had talked to her so much, and with such youthful ardor, of my literary ambitions and ideals, that I feared her ridicule; for another, my most eager hope was to surprise her with an opulent Christmas present. She, poor dear, was growing a trifle threadbare too; she had spoken, now and then, of some sort of fur neckpiece she had seen in shop windows; this, no less, was my secret ambition. And so, as the streets grew brighter with the approach of the day, and still the publisher delayed his remittance, I wrote him a masterly letter. It was coached in the form of a Christmas greeting from me to him; it acknowledged the validity of his contention that he had postponed a settlement because I was still submitting more and more masterpieces and he planned to settle en bloc; but it pointed out the supreme and tragic irony of my having to pass a Christmas in starvation and misery because I had spent so much time dispersing altruistic and factitious good will.

"As I waited anxiously for a reply, I was further disquieted by distressing behavior on Peggy's part. She had been rather strange with me for some time, which I attributed partly to my own shabby appearance and wretched preoccupation with my gruesome task. She had rallied me—some time before—on my mysterious mien, and I may have been clumsy in my retorts. Who can always know just the right accent with which to chaff a woman? At any rate, she had—with some suddenly assumed excuse of propriety—forbidden me the hospitality of her bedroom studio; even my portrait (which we had so blithely imagined as a national triumph in future years when we both stood at the crest of our arts) had been discontinued. We wandered the streets together, quarrelsome and unhappy; we could agree about nothing. In spite of this, I nourished my hopeful secret, still believing that when my check came, and enabled me to mark the Day of Days with the coveted fur, all would be happier than ever.

"It was two days before Christmas, and you may elaborate the picture with all the traditional tints of Dickens pathos. It was cold and snowy and I was hungry, worried, and forlorn. I was walking along Eighth Street wondering whether I could borrow enough money to telegraph to Chicago. Just by the Brevoort I met Peggy, and to my chagrin and despair she was wearing a beautiful new fur neckpiece—a tippet, I think they used to call them in those days. She looked a different girl: her face was pink, her small chin nestled adorably into the fur collar, her eyes were bright and merry. Well, I was only human, and I guess I must have shown my wretched disappointment. Of course she hadn't known that I hoped to surprise her in just that way, and when I blurted out something to that effect, she spoke tartly.

" 'You!' she cried. 'How could you buy me anything like that? I suppose you'd like me to tramp around in the snow all winter and catch my death of cold!'

"In spite of all the Christmas homilies I had written about good will and charity and what not, I lost my temper.

" 'Ah,' I said bitterly, 'I see it all now! I wasn't prosperous enough, so you've found someone else who can afford to buy furs for you. That's why you've kept me away from the studio, eh? You've got some other chap on the string.'

"I can still see her little flushed face, rosy with wind and snow, looking ridiculously stricken as she stood on that wintry corner. She began to say something, but I was hot with the absurd rage of youth. All my weeks of degradation on Gay Street suddenly boiled up in my mind. I was grotesquely melodramatic and absurd.

" 'A rich lover!" I sneered. 'Go ahead and take him! I'll stick to poverty and my ideals. You can have the furs and fleshpots!'

"Well, you never know how a woman will take things. To my utter amazement, instead of flaming up with anger, she burst into tears. But I was too proud and troubled to comfort her.

" 'Yes, you're right,' she sobbed. 'I had such fine dreams, but I couldn't stick it out. I'm not worthy of your ideals. I guess I've sold myself.' She turned and ran away down the slippery street, leaving me flabbergasted.

"I walked around and around Washington Square, not knowing what to do. She had as good as admitted that she had thrown me over for some richer man. And yet I didn't feel like giving her up without a struggle. Perhaps it all sounds silly now, but it was terribly real then.

"At last I went back to Gay Street. On the hall table was a letter from the publisher, with a check for fifty dollars. He had accepted fifty of the hundred or so pieces I had sent, and said if I would consider going to Chicago he would give me a position on his staff as Assistant Greeting Editor. 'Get into a good sound business,' he wrote. 'There will never be a panic in the Greeting line.'

"When I read that letter I was too elated to worry about anything. I would be able to fix things with Peggy somehow. I would say to her, in a melting voice, 'My Peggy is

(Reproduced by permission.
Copyright 1945 by The New Yorker Magazine, Inc.)

a young thing,' and she would tumble. She must love me still, or she wouldn't have cried. I rushed round to her lodging house, and went right upstairs without giving her a chance to deny me. I knocked, and when she came to the door she looked frightened and ill. She tried to stop me, but I burst in and waved the letter in front of her.

" 'Look at this, Peggy darling,' I shouted. 'We're going to be rich and infamous. I didn't tell you what I was doing, because I was afraid you'd be ashamed of me, after all my talk about high ideals. But anything is better than starving and freezing on Gay Street, or doing without the fur that pretty girls need.'

"She read the letter, and looked up at me with the queerest face.

" 'Now no more nonsense about the other man,' I said. 'I'll buy you a fur for Christmas that'll put his among camphor balls. Who is he, anyway?'

"She surprised me again, for this time she began to laugh.

" 'It's the same one,' she said. 'I mean, the same publisher—your friend in Chicago. Oh Dove, I've been doing drawings for Christmas cards, and I think they must be yours.'

"It was true. Her poor little cold studio was littered with sketches for Christmas drawings—blazing fires and ruddy Georgian squires with tankards of hissing ale and girls in sprigged muslin being coy under the mistletoe. And when she showed me the typewritten verses the publisher had sent her to illustrate, they were mine, sure enough. She had

had her check a day sooner than I, and had rushed off to buy herself the fur her heart yearned for.

" 'I was so ashamed doing the work,' she said—with her head on my waistcoat—'that I didn't dare tell you.' "

Dove sighed, and leaned back in his chair. A drizzle of rain and sleet tinkled on the window pane, but the fire was a core of rosy light.

"Not much of a Christmas story, eh?" he said. "Do you wonder, now, that I hesitate to look back at the cards I wrote and Peggy illustrated?"

"But what happened?" I asked. "It seems a nice enough story as far as you've gone."

"Peggy was a naughty little hypocrite," he said. "I found out that she wasn't really ashamed of illustrating my Greetings at all. She thought they were lovely. She honestly did. And presently she told me she simply couldn't marry a man who would capitalize Christmas. She said it was too sacred."

"I'm afraid this is the last Christmas we'll be able to use it."

"Could I have a raise, sir? My wife and kids believe me."

(Reprinted from Collier's by permission.)

The Errors of Santa Claus

STEPHEN LEACOCK

IT WAS CHRISTMAS EVE.

The Browns, who lived in the adjoining house, had been dining with the Joneses.

Brown and Jones were sitting over wine and walnuts at table. The others had gone upstairs.

"What are you giving to your boy for Christmas?" asked Brown.

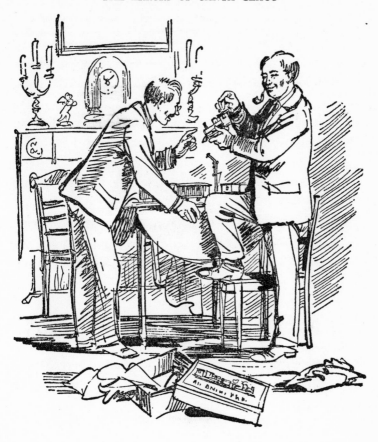

"A train," said Jones, "new kind of thing—automatic."

"Let's have a look at it," said Brown.

Jones fetched a parcel from the sideboard and began unwrapping it.

"Ingenious thing, isn't it?" he said, "goes on its own rails. Queer how kids love to play with trains, isn't it?"

"Yes," assented Brown, "how are the rails fixed?"

"Wait, I'll show you," said Jones, "just help me to shove these dinner things aside and roll back the cloth. There! See! You lay the rails like that and fasten them at the ends, so—"

"Oh, yes, I catch on, makes a grade, doesn't it? Just the thing to amuse a child, isn't it? I got Willie a toy aero plane."

"I know, they're great. I got Edwin one on his birthday. But I thought I'd get him a train this time. I told him Santa Claus was going to bring him something altogether new this time. Edwin, of course, believes in Santa Claus absolutely. Say, look at this locomotive, would you? It has a spring coiled up inside the fire box."

"Wind her up," said Brown with great interest, "so we can see her go."

"All right," said Jones, "just pile up two or three plates or something to lean the end of the rails on. There, notice the way it buzzes before it starts. Isn't that a great thing for a kid, eh?"

"Yes," said Brown, "and say! see this little string to pull the whistle. By Gad, it toots, eh? Just like real?"

"Now then, Brown," Jones went on, "you hitch on those cars and I'll start her. I'll be engineer, eh!"

Half an hour later Brown and Jones were still playing trains on the dining-room table.

But their wives upstairs in the drawing room hardly noticed their absence. They were too much interested.

"Oh, I think it's perfectly sweet," said Mrs. Brown, "just the loveliest doll I've seen in years. I must get one like it for Ulvina. Won't Clarisse be perfectly enchanted?"

"Yes," answered Mrs. Jones, "and then she'll have all the fun of arranging the dresses. Children love that so much. Look! there are three little dresses with the doll, aren't they cute? All cut out and ready to stitch together."

"Oh, how perfectly lovely," exclaimed Mrs. Brown, "I think the mauve one would suit the doll best—don't you? —with such golden hair—only don't you think it would make it much nicer to turn back the collar, so, and to put a little band—so?"

"*What* a good idea!" said Mrs. Jones, "do let's try it. Just wait, I'll get a needle in a minute. I'll tell Clarisse that Santa Claus sewed it himself. The child believes in Santa Claus absolutely."

And half an hour later Mrs. Jones and Mrs. Brown were so busy stitching doll's clothes that they could not hear the roaring of the little train up and down the dining table, and had no idea what the four children were doing.

Nor did the children miss their mothers.

"Dandy, aren't they?" Edwin Jones was saying to little Willie Brown, as they sat in Edwin's bedroom. "A hundred in a box, with cork tips, and see, an amber mouthpiece that fits into a little case at the side. Good present for dad, eh?"

"Fine!" said Willie appreciatively, "I'm giving father cigars."

"I know, I thought of cigars too. Men always like cigars

and cigarettes. You can't go wrong on them. Say, would you like to try one or two of these cigarettes? We can take them from the bottom. You'll like them, they're Russian, —away ahead of Egyptian."

"Thanks," answered Willie. "I'd like one immensely. I only started smoking last spring—on my twelfth birthday. I think a feller's a fool to begin smoking cigarettes too soon, don't you? It stunts him. I waited till I was twelve."

"Me too," said Edwin, as they lighted their cigarettes. "In fact, I wouldn't buy them now if it weren't for dad. I simply *had* to give him something from Santa Claus. He believes in Santa Claus absolutely, you know."

And while this was going on, Clarisse was showing little Ulvina the absolutely lovely little bridge set that she got for her mother. "Aren't these markers perfectly charming?" said Ulvina, "and don't you love this little Dutch design—or is it Flemish, darling?"

"Dutch," said Clarisse, "isn't it quaint? And aren't these the dearest little things—for putting the money in when you play. I needn't have got them with it—they'd have sold the rest separately—but I think it's too utterly slow playing without money, don't you?"

"Oh, abominable," shuddered Ulvina, "but your mamma never plays for money, does she?"

"Mamma! Oh, gracious, no. Mamma's far too slow for that. But I shall tell her that Santa Claus insisted on putting in the little money boxes."

"I suppose she believes in Santa Claus, just as my Mamma does."

"Oh, absolutely," said Clarisse, and added, "What if we play a little game! With a double dummy, the French way, or Norwegian Skat, if you like. That only needs two."

"All right," agreed Ulvina, and in a few minutes they were deep in a game of cards with a little pile of pocket money beside them.

About half an hour later, all the members of the two families were down again in the drawing room. But of course nobody said anything about the presents. In any case they were all too busy looking at the beautiful big Bible, with maps in it, that the Joneses had bought to give to Grandfather. They all agreed that with the help of it, Grandfather could hunt up any place in Palestine, in a moment, day or night.

But upstairs, away upstairs in a sitting room of his own, Grandfather Jones was looking with an affectionate eye at the presents that stood beside him. There was a beautiful whiskey decanter, with silver filigree outside (and whiskey inside) for Jones, and for the little boy a big nickel-plated jew's-harp.

Later on, far in the night, the person, or the influence, or whatever it is called Santa Claus, took all the presents and placed them in the people's stockings.

And, being blind as he always has been, he gave the

wrong things to the wrong people—in fact, he gave them just as indicated above.

But the next day, in the course of Christmas morning, the situation straightened itself out, just as it always does.

Indeed, by ten o'clock, Brown and Jones were playing with the train, and Mrs. Brown and Mrs. Jones were making dolls' clothes, and the boys were smoking cigarettes, and Clarisse and Ulvina were playing cards for their pocket money.

And upstairs—away up—Grandfather was drinking whiskey and playing the jew's-harp.

And so Christmas, just as it always does, turned out all right after all.

HUBERT

"Getting laid off on Christmas Eve—how's THAT for
a Christmas present, eh?"

(Reprinted by permission.
Copyright 1952 by King Features Syndicate, Inc.)

153

Ring Out, Wild Bells

D. B. WYNDHAM LEWIS

NOTHING COULD BE MORE FESTIVE THAN THE BREAKFAST-room at Merryweather Hall this noontide of 29th December. On the hearth a huge crackling fire bade defiance to the rain which lashed the tall French windows. The panelled walls were gay with holly and mistletoe and paper decorations of every hue. On the long sideboard were displayed eggs in conjunction with ham, bacon, and sausages, also boiled and scrambled; kedgeree, devilled kidneys, chops, grilled herrings, sole, and haddock, cold turkey, cold goose, cold grouse, cold game pie, cold ham, cold beef, brawn, potted shrimps, a huge Stilton, fruit of every kind, rolls, toast, tea, and coffee, all simmering on silver heaters or tempting the healthy appetite from huge crested salvers. Brooding over all this with an evil leer, the butler, Mr. Banks, looked up to see a youngish guest with drawn and yellow face, shuddering violently.

'Breakfast, sir?' asked Banks, rubbing his hands.

The guest, a Mr. Reginald Parable, nodded and held out his palm. Banks shook into it two tablets from a small bottle.

'They're all in the library,' said Banks, pouring half a tumbler of water. 'Cor, what they look like—well,' said Banks, chuckling, 'it's just too bad.'

Mr. Parable finished breakfast in one swallow and went along to the library. In every arm-chair, and lying against each other on every settee, eyes closed, faces worn with misery, each wearing a paper cap from a cracker, lay Squire Merryweather's guests. The squire believed in a real old-fashioned Christmas, and for five days now his guests had tottered, stiff with eating, from table to chair, only to be roused by the jovial squire with a festive roar ten minutes later.

The countryside was under water; and as nobody could go out from morning to night, Squire Merryweather could, and did, devise every kind of merrie old-time entertainment for his raving guests.

Thunderous distant chuckles as Mr. Parable wavered into the only unoccupied corner of a huge leather settee announced that the squire had been consulting his secret store of books of merriment once more. And even as Mr. Parable hastily turned to feign epilepsy in his corner, Squire Merryweather bustled in.

'Morning,' said a weak voice, that of Lord Lymph.

'Wake all these people up,' said the squire.

When everybody was awake the squire said: 'Colonel Rollick has five daughters, Gertrude, Mabel, Pamela, Edith, and Hilda. Mabel is half the age that Gertrude and Edith were when Hilda and Mabel were respectively twice and one-and-a-half times as old as Pamela will be on 8th May 1940. Wait a minute—that's right, 8th May. Every time the colonel takes his five daughters to town for the day it costs him three pounds fifteen and eight-pence-halfpenny in railway fares, first return. One Christmas night Colonel Rollick says to his guests: "Let's play rectangles." "I don't know how it's played," says old Mrs. Cheeryton, who happens to be present. "Why," says the colonel, "like this: we get the Ague-Browns to drop in, and form ourselves into four units, the square on the hypotenuse of which is equal to the sum of the squares on the——" '

At this point a lovely, lazy, deep-voiced blonde, Mrs. Wallaby-Threep, roused herself sufficiently to produce a dainty pearl-handled revolver from her corsage and fire at Squire Merryweather twice, missing him each time.

'Eh? Who spoke?' asked the squire abruptly, without

raising his eyes from *Ye Merrie Christmasse Puzzle-Booke.*

'Tiny Tim,' replied Mrs. Wallaby-Threep, taking one more shot. This time, however, she missed as before.

'You probably took too much of a pull on the trigger,' murmured the rector with a deprecating smile. The squire was patron of the living and he felt a duty towards his guests.

'I'll get him yet,' said Mrs. Wallaby-Threep.

'CHARADES!' shouted Squire Merryweather suddenly, waving a sprig of holly in his right hand.

'Again?' said a querulous Old Etonian voice. It was that of Mr. Egbert Frankleigh, the famous gentleman-novelist, who wanted to tell more stories. Since Christmas Eve there had been five story-telling sessions, each guest supplying some tale of romance, adventure, mystery, or plain bore-dom. After every story the squire had applauded loudly and called for wassail, frumenty, old English dances, and merry-making—even after two very peculiar stories about obsessional neuroses told by two sombre young Oxford men, Mr. Ebbing and Mr. Crafter, both of whom took hashish with Avocado pears, wore black suède shoes, and practised Mithraism.

'Charades!' roared Squire Merryweather, tucking his book under his arm and rubbing his hands with a roar of laughter. 'Hurrah! Come along, everybody. Jump to it, boys and girls! This is going to be fun! Two of you, quick!'

A choking snore from poor old Lady Emily Wainscot, who was quite worn out (she died the following week, greatly regretted), was the only reply. Fourteen pairs of lack-lustre-ringed-with-blue eyes stared at him in haggard silence.

'Eh? What?' asked the squire, more bewildered than hurt.

'You said *charades*, sir?' said Mr. Ebbing. 'We shall be delighted to assist!'

Booming like a happy bull, the squire flung an arm round each of the two young men and danced them out of the room.

'Me for the hay,' said Mrs. Wallaby-Threep, snuggling into a cushion and closing her eyes. The rest of the company were not slow to follow suit. Very soon all were asleep, and snoring yelps and groans filled the library of Merryweather Hall.

It was bright, sunshiny daylight when the banging of the gong by the second footman roused the squire's guests from nearly twenty-four hours of deep, refreshing sleep. The sardonic Banks stood before them. He seemed angry, and addressed himself to Lord Lymph.

'I just found the squire's body in a wardrobe trunk, my lord.'

'In a *trunk*, Banks?'

'That's all right,' said Lady Ura Treate, yawning. 'It's an old Oxford trick. Body in a trunk. All these neurotics do it. Where *are* those two sweet chaps, Banks?'

'They've hopped it, my lady.'

'Well, that's all right, Banks,' said Freddie Slouche. 'Body in trunk. Country-house mystery. Quite normal.'

As he spoke, the guests, chattering happily, were already streaming out to order the packing and see to their cars. In a few moments only Banks and Mr. Parable were left in the room. Banks seemed aggrieved.

'It's all pretty damn fine, Mr. Whoosis, but who gets it in the neck when the cops get down? Who'll be under suspicion as per usual? Who always is? The butler! Me!'

'Just an occupational risk,' said Mr. Parable, politely.

'It would be if I wasn't a bit smart,' said Banks.

Mr. Parable nodded and hurried out as the servants began looting the hall.

FROM NINE TO FIVE By Jo Fischer

Where do I return these Christmas presents so I can find
out how much they cost?

How Come Christmas?

ROARK BRADFORD

Scene: Corner in rural Negro church by the stove. The stove is old, and the pipe is held approximately erect by guy wires, but a cheerful fire is evident through cracks in the stove, and the wood box is well filled. Six children sit on a bench which has been shifted to face the stove, and the Reverend stands between them and the stove. A hatrack on the wall supports sprigs of holly and one "plug" hat. A window is festooned with holly, long strips of red paper, and strings of popcorn. A small Christmas bell and a tiny American flag are the only "store bought" decorations.

REVEREND:

Well, hyar we is, chilluns, and hyar hit is Christmas. Now we all know we's hyar 'cause hit's Christmas, don't we? But what I want to know is, who gonter tell me how come hit's Christmas?

WILLIE:

'Cause old Sandy Claus come around about dis time er de year, clawin' all de good chilluns wid presents.

CHRISTINE:

Dat ain't right, is hit, Revund? Hit's Christmas 'cause de Poor Little Jesus was bawned on Christmas, ain't hit, Revund?

REVEREND:

Well, bofe er dem is mighty good answers. Old Sandy Claus do happen around about dis time er de year wid presents, and de Poor Little Jesus sho was bawned on Christmas Day. Now, de question is, did old Sandy Claus start clawin' chilluns wid presents before de Poor Little Jesus got bawned, or did de Little Jesus git bawned before old Sandy Claus started gittin' around?

WILLIE:

I bet old Sandy Claus was clawin' chilluns before de Poor Little Jesus started studdin' about gittin' bawned.

CHRISTINE:

Naw, suh. De Little Jesus comed first, didn't he, Revund?

WILLIE:

Old Sandy Claus is de oldest. I seed his pitchers and I seed Jesus' pitchers and old Sandy Claus is a heap de oldest. His whiskers mighty nigh tetch de ground.

DELIA:

Dat ain't right. Old Methuselah is de oldest, ain't he, Revund? 'Cause de Bible say

> Methuselah was de oldest man of his time.
> He lived nine hund'ed and sixty-nine.
> And he died and went to heaven in due time.

REVEREND:

Methuselah was powerful old, all right.

WILLIE:

He wa'n't no older den old Sandy Claus, I bet. Old Sandy Claus got a heap er whiskers.

CHRISTINE:

But de Poor Little Jesus come first. He was hyar before old man Methuselah, wa'n't he, Revund?

REVEREND:

He been hyar a powerful long time, all right.

WILLIE:

So has old Sandy Claus. He got powerful long whiskers.

DELIA:

Moses got a heap er whiskers too.

REVEREND:

Yeah, Moses was a mighty old man, too, but de p'int is, how come Christmas git started bein' Christmas? Now who gonter tell me? 'Cause hyar hit is Christmas Day, wid

ev'ybody happy and rejoicin' about, and hyar is us, settin'
by de stove in de wa'm churchhouse, tawkin' about hit.
But ain't nobody got no idee how come hit start bein'
Christmas?

WILLIE:

You can' fool old Sandy Claus about Christmas. He
know, don't he, Revund? He jest lay around and watch
and see how de chilluns mind dey maw, and den de fust
thing you know he got his mind make up about who been
good and who been bad, and den he just hauls off and
has hisse'f Christmas.

CHRISTINE:

Yeah, but how come he know hit's time to haul off and
have hisse'f a Christmas?

WILLIE:

'Cause any time old Sandy Claus make up his mind to
have Christmas, well, who gonter stop him?

CHRISTINE:

Den how come he don't never make up his mind ontwell
de middle er winter? How come he don't make up his
mind on the Fou'th er July? Ev'body git good around
de Fou'th er July, jest like Christmas, so's dey kin go to
de picnic. But Sandy Claus ain't payin' no mind to dat
cause hit ain't time for Christmas, is hit, Revund?

WILLIE:

'Cou'se he don't have Christmas on de Fou'th er July.
'Cause hit ain't no p'int in Sandy Claus clawin' ev'ybody
when ev'ybody's goin' to de picnic, anyhow. Sandy Claus
b'lieve in scatterin' de good stuff out, don't he, Revund?

He say, "Well, hit ain't no p'int in me clawin' fo'ks when dey already havin' a good time goin' to de picnic. Maybe I better wait to de dead er winter when hit's too cold for de picnic." Ain't dat right, Revund?

REVEREND:

Sandy Claus do b'lieve in scatterin de good stuff about de seasons, Willie, and hit sho ain't no p'int in havin' Christmas on de Fou'th er July. 'Cause de Fou'th er July is got hit's own p'int. And who gonter tell me what de p'int er de Fou'th er July is:

CHORUS:

> Old Gawge Wash'n'ton whupped de kaing,
> And de eagle squalled, Let Freedom ring.

REVEREND:

Dat's right. And dat was in de summertime, so ev'ybody went out and had a picnic 'cause dey was so glad dat Gawge Wash'n'ton whupped dat kaing. Now what's de p'int er Christmas?

WILLIE:

Old Sandy Claus . . .

CHRISTINE:

De Poor Little Jesus . . .

REVEREND:

Well, hit seem like old Sandy Claus and de Poor Little Jesus bofe is mixed up in dis thing, f'm de way y'all chilluns looks at hit. And I reckon y'all is just about 'zackly right too. 'Cause dat's how hit is. Bofe of 'em is so mixed up in hit I can't tell which is which, hardly.

DELIA:

Was dat before de Fou'th er July?

CHRISTINE:

Cou'se hit was. Don't Christmas always come before de Fou'th er July?

WILLIE:

Naw, suh. Hit's de Fou'th er July fust, and den hit's Christmas. Ain't dat right, Revund?

REVEREND:

I b'lieve Christine got you dat time, Willie. Christmas do come before de Fou'th er July. 'Cause you see hit was at Christmas when old Gawge Wash'n'ton got mad at de kaing 'cause de kaing was gonter kill de Poor Little Jesus. And him and de kaing fit f'm Christmas to de Fou'th er July before old Gawge Wash'n'ton finally done dat kaing up.

WILLIE:

And Gawge Wash'n'ton whupped dat kaing, didn't he?

REVEREND:

He whupped de stuffin' outn him. He whupped him f'm Balmoral to Belial and den back again. He jest done dat kaing up so bad dat he jest natchally put kaingin' outn style, and ev'y since den, hit ain't been no more kaings to 'mount to much.

You see, kaings was bad fo'ks. Dey was mean. Dey'd druther kill you den leave you alone. You see a kaing wawkin' down de road, and you better light out across de field, 'cause de kaing would wawk up and chop yo' haid off. And de law couldn't tetch him, 'cause he was de kaing.

"We better break this up. We're straining their credulity."

So all de fo'ks got skeered er de kaing, 'cause dey didn't know how to do nothin' about hit. So ev'ybody went around, tryin' to stay on de good side of him. And all er dat is how come de Poor Little Jesus and Old Sandy Claus got mixed up wid gittin' Christmas goin'.

You see, one time hit was a little baby bawned name' de Poor Little Jesus, but didn't nobody know dat was his name yit. Dey knew he was a powerful smart and powerful purty little baby, but dey didn't know his name was de Poor Little Jesus. So, 'cause he was so smart and so purty, ev'ybody thought he was gonter grow up and be de kaing. So quick as dat news got spread around, ev'ybody jest about bust to git on de good side er de baby, 'cause dey figure efn de start soon enough he'd grow up likin' 'em and not chop dey haids off.

So old Moses went over and give him a hund'ed dollars in gold. And old Methuselah went over and give him a diamond ring. And old Peter give him a fine white silk robe. And ev'ybody was runnin' in wid fine presents so de Poor Little Jesus wouldn't grow up and chop de haids off.

Ev'ybody but old Sandy Claus. Old Sandy Claus was kind er old and didn't git around much, and he didn't hyar de news dat de Poor Little Jesus was gonter grow up and be de kaing. So him and de old lady was settin' back de fire one night, toastin' dey shins and tawkin' about dis and dat, when old Miz Sandy Claus up and remark, she say, "Sandy, I hyars Miss Mary got a brand new baby over at her house."

"Is dat a fack?" says Sandy Claus. "Well, well, hit's a mighty cold night to do anything like dat, ain't hit? But on de yuther hand, he'll be a heap er pleasure and fun for her next summer I reckon."

So de tawk went on, and finally old Sandy Claus remark dat hit was powerful lonesome around de house since all er de chilluns growed and married off.

"Dey all married well," say Miz Sandy Claus, "and so I say, 'Good ruddance.' You ain't never had to git up and cyore dey colic and mend dey clothes, so you gittin' lonesome. Me, I love 'em all, but I'm glad dey's married and doin' well."

So de tawk run on like dat for a while, and den old Sandy Claus got up and got his hat. "I b'lieve," he say, "I'll drop over and see how dat baby's gittin' along. I ain't seed no chilluns in so long I'm pyore hongry to lean my eyes up agin a baby."

"You ain't goin' out on a night like dis, is you?" say Miz Sandy Claus.

"Sho I'm goin' out on a night like dis," say Sandy Claus. "I'm pyore cravin' to see some chilluns."

"But hit's snowin' and goin' on," say Miz Sandy Claus. "You know yo' phthisic been devilin' you, anyhow, and you'll git de chawley mawbuses sloppin' around in dis weather."

"No mind de tawk," say Sandy Claus. "Git me my umbrella and my overshoes. And you better git me a little somethin' to take along for a cradle gift, too, I reckon."

"You know hit ain't nothin' in de house for no cradle gift," say Miz Sandy Claus.

"Git somethin'," say Sandy Claus. "You got to give a new baby somethin', or else you got bad luck. Get me one er dem big red apples outn de kitchen."

"What kind er cradle gift is an apple?" say Miz Sandy Claus. "Don't you reckon dat baby git all de apples he want?"

"Git me de apple," say Sandy Claus. "Hit ain't much, one way you looks at hit. But f'm de way dat baby gonter look at de apple, hit'll be a heap."

So Sandy Claus got de apple and he lit out.

Well, when he got to Miss Mary's house ev'ybody was standin' around givin' de Poor Little Jesus presents. Fine presents. Made outn gold and silver and diamonds and silk, and all like dat. Dey had de presents stacked around dat baby so high you couldn't hardly see over 'em. So when ev'ybody seed old Sandy Claus come in dey looked to see what he brang. And when dey seed he didn't brang nothin' but a red apple, dey all laughed.

"Quick as dat boy grows up and gits to be de kaing," dey told him, "he gonter chop yo' haid off."

"No mind dat," say Sandy Claus. "Y'all jest stand back." And so he went up to de crib and he pushed away a handful er gold and silver and diamonds and stuff, and handed de Poor Little Jesus dat red apple. "Hyar, son," he say, "take dis old apple. See how she shines?"

And de Poor Little Jesus reached up and grabbed dat

apple in bofe hands, and laughed jest as brash as you please!

Den Sandy Claus tuck and tickled him under de chin wid his before finger, and say, "Goodly-goodly-goodly." And de Poor Little Jesus laughed some more and he reached up and grabbed a fist full er old Sandy Claus' whiskers, and him and old Sandy Claus went round and round!

So about dat time, up stepped de Lawd. "I swear, old Sandy Claus," say de Lawd. "Betwixt dat apple and dem whiskers, de Poor Little Jesus ain't had so much fun since he been bawn."

So Sandy Claus stepped back and bowed low and give de Lawd hy-dy, and say, "I didn't know ev'ybody was chivareein', or else I'd a stayed at home. I didn't had nothin' much to bring dis time, 'cause you see how hit's been dis year. De dry weather and de bull weevils got mighty nigh all de cotton, and de old lady been kind er puny——"

"Dat's all right, Sandy," say de Lawd. "Gold and silver have I a heap of. But verily you sho do know how to handle you'se'f around de chilluns."

"Well, Lawd," say Sandy Claus, "I don't know much about chilluns. Me and de old lady raised up fou'teen. But she done most er de work. Me, I jest likes 'em and I manages to git along wid 'em."

"You sho do git along wid 'em good," say de Lawd.

"Hit's easy to do what you likes to do," say Sandy Claus.

"Well," say de Lawd, "hit might be somethin' in dat, too. But de trouble wid my world is, hit ain't enough people which likes to do de right thing. But you likes to do wid chilluns, and dat's what I needs. So stand still and shet yo' eyes whilst I passes a miracle on you."

So Sandy Claus stood still and shet his eyes, and de Lawd r'ared back and passed a miracle on him and say, "Old Sandy Claus, live forever, and make my chilluns happy."

So Sandy Claus opened his eyes and say, "Thank you kindly, Lawd. But do I got to keep 'em happy all de time? Dat's a purty big job. Hit's be a heap er fun, but still and at de same time—"

"Yeah, I knows about chilluns, too," say de Lawd. "Chilluns got to fret and git in devilment ev'y now and den and git a whuppin', f'm dey maw, or else dey skin won't git loose so's dey kin grow. But you jest keep yo' eyes on 'em and make 'em all happy about once a year. How's dat?"

"Dat's fine," say Sandy Claus. "Hit'll be a heap er fun, too. What time er de year you speck I better make 'em happy, Lawd?"

"Christmas suit me," say de Lawd, "efn hit's all O.K. wid you."

"Hit's jest about right for me," say old Sandy Claus.

So ev'y since dat day and time old Sandy Claus been clawin' de chilluns on Christmas, and dat's on de same day dat de Poor Little Jesus got bawned. 'Cause dat's de way de Lawd runs things. O' cou'se de Lawd knowed hit wa'n't gonter be long before de Poor Little Jesus growed up and got to be a man. And when he done dat, all de grown fo'ks had him so's dey c'd moan they sins away and lay they burdens down on him, and git happy in they hearts. De Lawd made Jesus for de grown fo'ks. But de Lawd know de chilluns got to have some fun, too, so dat's how come hit's Sandy Claus and Christmas and all.

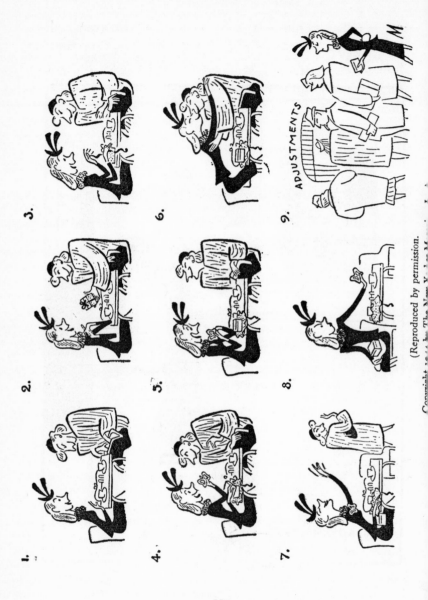

ADJUSTMENTS

MOPSY　　　　　　By Gladys Parker

(The Associated Newspapers, Inc.)

175

A Hint for Next Christmas

A. A. MILNE

OBVIOUSLY THERE SHOULD BE A STANDARD VALUE FOR A certain type of Christmas present. One may give what one will to one's own family or particular friends; that is all right. But in a Christmas house-party there is a pleasant interchange of parcels, of which the string and the brown paper and the kindly thought are the really important ingredients, and the gift inside is nothing more than an excuse for those things. It is embarrassing for you if Jones has apologized for his brown paper with a hundred cigars and you have only excused yourself with twenty-five cigarettes; perhaps still more embarrassing if it is you who have lost so heavily on the exchange. An understanding that the contents were to be worth five shillings exactly would avoid this embarrassment.

And now I am reminded of the ingenuity of a friend of mine, William by name, who arrived at a large country house for Christmas without any present in his bag. He had expected neither to give nor to receive anything but to his horror he discovered on the 24th that everybody was preparing a Christmas present for him, and that it was taken for granted that he would require a little privacy and brown paper on Christmas Eve for the purpose of addressing his own offerings to others. He had wild thoughts of telegraphing to London for something to be sent down, and spoke to other members of the house-party in order to discover what sort of presents would be suitable.

"What are you giving our host?" he asked one of them.

"Mary and I are giving him a book," said John, referring to his wife.

William then approached the youngest son of the house, and discovered that he and his next brother Dick were sharing in this, that, and the other. When he had heard this, William retired to his room and thought profoundly.

He was the first down to breakfast on Christmas morning. All the places at the table were piled high with presents. He looked at John's place. The top parcel said, "To John and Mary from Charles." William took out his fountain-pen and added a couple of words to the inscription. It then read, "To John and Mary from Charles and William," and in William's opinion looked just as effective as before. He moved on to the next place. "To Angela from Father," said the top parcel. "And William," wrote William. At his hostess' place he hesitated for a moment. The first present there was for "Darling Mother, from her loving children." It did not seem that an "and William" was quite suitable. But his hostess was not to be deprived of William's kindly thought; twenty seconds later the handkerchiefs "from John and Mary and William" expressed all the nice things he was feeling for her. He passed on to the next place . . .

It is of course impossible to thank every donor of a joint gift; one simply thanks the first person whose eyes one happens to catch. Sometimes William's eye was caught, sometimes not. But he was spared all embarrassment; and I can recommend his solution of the problem with perfect confidence to those who may be in a similar predicament next Christmas.

Came the Dawn

THIS IS THE TRUE PLACE TO SPEAK OF THE PROPERTIES OF chocolate flavored with amber; properties which I have verified by many experiments, the result of which I am proud to lay before my readers. Listen, then:

Let any man who shall have drunk too deeply of the cup of pleasure, or given to work too many of the hours which should belong to sleep; who shall find the accustomed polish of his wits turned to dullness, feel damp oppression in the air and time hanging heavily, or be tortured by a fixed idea which robs him of all liberty of thought; let all such, we say, administer to themselves a good pint of Ambered Chocolate, allowing from sixty to seventy-two grains of amber to a pound, and they will see marvels.

In my own particular way of specifying things, I call ambered chocolate the chocolate of the afflicted.

J. A. Brillat-Savarin.

"Merry Christmas!"